Many thanks to Chris and Dena
for their parts in making this book happen

Food and Feast

in the
World of the Blue Bells Chronicles

a
gastronomic historic poetic musical
romp in thyme

By

Laura Vosika

G/H

Gabriel's Horn Publishing

Contact: editors@gabrielshornpress.com

Published in Minneapolis, Minnesota by Gabriel's Horn Publishing

Cover design by Laura Vosika
Author Photo Emmanuel's Light Photography, by Chris Powell

First printing October 2016
Printed in the United States of America

For sales, please contact editors@gabrielshornpress.com

ISBN-10: 1-938990-24-2
ISBN-13: 978-1-938990-24-3

Acknowledgments

No book is complete without acknowledging those who have done so much to make the book happen.

My thanks to Chris Powell, who has been a great source of encouragement and help for the *Blue Bells* story, and has bought and cooked some of the recipes in this book while I continued to write and edit it.

A huge thank you to DW for his help tracking down original French recipes from *Le Managier de Paris,* and to Caoimhe Stack, for her translations.

Thank you as always to the Night Writers—Ross, Judy, Lyn, Genny, Judd, Janet, Stephanie, Sue, Catherine, and Meredythe— for years of listening to Shawn's story, and your great input.

My thanks to Dena Rose, my publicist, who encouraged me in this and has done so much for me this year, including making some of the meals in the book.

Table of Contents

I Cokaigne is met and drink
Wiþvte care, how, and swink;
þe met is trie, þe drink is clere,
To none, russin, and sopper...

~ The Land of Cokaygne, c. 1330

Appetizer/Forward

Warning: This is not a cookbook!

Yes, this is a book with many recipes in it. However, I am a musician, author, and historical researcher. This book is a collection of research for my novels, with food, in this case, being the focus of the research. Thus, it is also a book of the history and lore of the time. Some of the recipes have been given in modern terms, some in their original form.

Food and Feast in the World of the Blue Bells Chronicles came about because a reader was taken with the foods described in the books, and asked for such a book. It has been fun and educational for me to delve more deeply into cuisine and gastronomy as its own subject.

When I set out on this venture, I thought the difficulty would be finding authentic medieval recipes. Rather, thanks to the wonder of the internet and my growing collection of historical cookbooks (a little irony for someone who has been known to have microwave popcorn for dinner after a long day) the difficulty has been *paring down* (no cooking pun intended there!) all that is available to what can fit in one book! I would dearly love to publish a book with *all* my findings, but such a book would not fit into a single binding.

This book is organized around chronological scenes from the first four books of *The Blue Bells Chronicles*. The *Blue Bells Chronicles* is a tale of time travel, mysteries and miracles, romance and redemption, as Shawn Kleiner, modern trombonist, a gambling, drinking, arrogant womanizer, and Niall Campbell, devout, responsible medieval warrior and harper, switch places in time. Shawn finds himself caught in medieval Scotland, where his money and power no longer get him out of the trouble he excels at getting himself into.

Thus, in *Food and Feast,* you will find bare bones medieval 'receipts' in middle English, measurements set to medieval recipes, Scottish recipes, recipes from Midwest America, and 'survival' recipes, as Shawn and Niall eat during their travels in the wilderness or with the medieval Scottish army of James Douglas.

You will find thoughts from Hildegard von Bingen, medieval mystic, author, scientist, visionary, abbess, composer, and playwright, on food, diet, and health. Despite our belief that we have advanced, and know more than previous civilizations, Hildegard knew not only how various foods affect us physically, but how they affect us emotionally—a wisdom we have lost.

You will find poetry and song about food.

A disclaimer—yes, I'm disclaiming it again! I am not a cook. (You have been warned!) I am an author and musician. This means I'm *always* on time (Billy Joel even wrote a song about that!) but I probably show up with a cheap burger from MacDonald's. (And I don't mean the clan, despite Niall's confusion on that matter.) So, dare I say—take everything here with...a grain of salt. Or parsley, sage, rosemary, or thyme. (Oh, man, there's a song about *that,* too! Well, I did say this is a musical journey, in addition to culinary.)

Or, most especially (getting back to the topic of the previous paragraph after all those asides) take everything here with lots and lots of almonds. Almonds, I have discovered, were very popular in medieval cuisine. So yes, take everything you read here with lots of almonds!

So, continuing with the disclaiming: this is a book of research on how things were done. Yes, I give specific processes they used. However, I am an academic and a reporter of history, *not* a trained chef, (did I mention I'll show up on time but with a brown bag from MacDonald's?), survival expert, herbalist, winemaker, or brewer. *This is an introductory overview of these subjects.* Please dig into these more unusual things on your own before trying them yourself! If you plan to make ale, or wine, or herbal medicines, I strongly suggest talking to specialists in those subjects.

As another disclaimer, it is almost certainly illegal to eat porpoises today. Please do not make porpoise frumenty.

Introduction

Throughout history, cultures and people have varied widely, from peace-loving to warring, from French fashion of the 1700s to loin cloths, from vegans to cannibals, from those who spent a lifetime within a few square miles to those who set sail for unknown lands. Some things remain constant, however. Every culture has music, faith, and food.

This book talks about food—particularly medieval food. But there are a couple of things to clarify.

The first is that, saying *medieval food* is like saying, 'a modern dialect.' There are dialects that are modern as opposed to medieval, but there is no 'modern' dialect. The problem is much larger when speaking of 'medieval' anything, because the medieval era spans a thousand years (5th century to 15th century) and even when we narrow it to medieval Europe (as this book does), we're still talking about multiple countries spanning a continent and the surrounding islands, and we're still talking about a thousands years.

Narrowing things down helps. The early middle ages lasted from the 5th century to the 10th and the high middle ages from the 11th to the 13th century (1001 to 1300 are the traditional dates.) Niall lived on the cusp of the Late Middle Ages, which are traditionally dated 1301 to 1500. Much of what we have left in the form of written cookbooks dates from after his time, and to my knowledge there is no surviving written record of recipes from the Scottish Highlands of Niall's time.

Thus, the recipes here are speculative. We can make good guesses, based on later cookbooks, on having an idea what foods were available in Scotland, and noting that many foods have not necessarily changed a great deal, even into our modern times.

Indeed, one writer notes that the 'problem' with medieval cheese is that it will invariably underwhelm the adventurous seeking out exotic 'medieval' foods, because it's really not that different from what we eat today. Although he speaks of cheese, his words could be true of many dishes.

So what are some of our sources?

Given the lack of a printing press before 1440, the high rates of illiteracy, the fluid (forgive the choice of words) nature of so many soup and stew recipes, and the fact that recipes would have been passed from mother to daughter, from castle cook to apprentice, orally and as a way of life, it's not surprising there are relatively few cookbooks left to us from medieval times. And yet, the list is not completely short—not as short as a pastry puff. The following is only a partial list.

- *Anonymous Andalusian Cookbook,* 1200s
- *Enseignements qui enseingnent a apareillier toutes manieres de viandes*—a cookbook written by an unknown cook, in the time of Philip the Fair, 1268 -November 29, 1314
- *Utilis Coquinario,* 1300s
- Liber de Sent Sovi, 1300s
- *Le Viandier de Taillevent,* c. 1315-1395
- *Das Buch von guter Speise,* (c 1350) Written in rhyme
- *Forme of Cury,* c 1390
- *Le Managier de Paris,* c. 1393. This is not strictly a cookbook. It is a book on household management, written by a man for his young bride. It does however contain many recipes and is frequently referenced in books on historical cooking
- *Das Kochbuch des Meisters Eberhard,* early 1400s, German
- *Ein Kochbuch aus dem Archiv des Deutschen Ordens,* 1400s northeastern Germany
- Harleian manuscript 279, c. 1430
- Harleian manuscript 4016, c 1450
- *Alte Kochrezepte aus dem Bayerischen Inntal,* 1400s or 1500s, East Bavaria
- *Due Libre B* early 1400s, southern Italy
- *Due Fait de Cuisine*, 1420, Savoy
- *Liber cure cocorum,* ca. 1430 Another cookbook in rhyme
- *Wel ende edelike spijse* late 1400s
- *Das Kuchbuch der Sabrina Welserin*, 1553, German
- *La Varenne's Cookery* 1600s

We also learn about the cuisine of the past through court documents, household records, journals, fiction, poetry, and song.

Medieval Thoughts on Food and Cooking

Food has never been strictly utilitarian. Eating has, throughout history and across cultures, been a social affair, and people have devoted a great deal of energy to entire philosophies on what we eat, how we eat, on how various foods affect our health and moods.

In medieval times, the healing arts had three branches: surgery, pharmacy, and diet. (It should be noted that Hildegard von Bingen, a medieval mystic, abbess, diplomat, composer, and playwright, whom we will see throughout this book, would add a fourth branch: spiritual health.) Although the means of surgery and types of medicines have changed greatly, we still operate on largely the same four principles. In recent years, we are regaining a sense of the vital importance of what we eat, and how many foods are affecting us in ways we had not realized.

Today, we regard *diet* as something we do for a time to lose weight. In medieval times, it was looked on in more general terms as a concept of applying thought, reflection, and analysis to eating. A *diet* was not to lose weight, but a regiment of eating applied to specific illnesses or to the more general goal of keeping good health: *controlled,* conscious, healthy eating, to attain particular purposes—or porpoises...but weight...I mean wait, that comes later in the book. Yes, we'll get to porpoises!

The School of Salerno in Italy, has left us a text, written about 1060, *Flos medicinæ vel regimen sanitatis Salernitanum (Medicine according to the Salernitan regimen of health)*, which advises the reader on habits of hygiene and eating to maintain health. The School devised diets to adjust the tempers. Lethargic men should add spicy foods, for example, while hot-tempered men should eliminate them.

Much of medieval dietetics comes from the belief in the four humors. This philosophy came down to medieval Europe from pre-Socratic philosophy built on the idea of the four elementals—water, air, fire, and earth—to create a system of oppositions—hot and cold, dry and moist, bitter and sweet. Good health came from keeping these elements and opposites in good balance.

Interestingly, similar ideas arose in India and medieval Europe also received some of these ideas via the *Taqwim as-sihha (Table of contents of health),* written by Ibn Butlan, a Christian physician trained in Baghdad in the early to mid 11th century, and later translated into the Latin *Tacuinum sanitatis.* This book delves into a number of foods, spices, drinks, types of weather, aromas, and human activities, analyzing them according to hot, cold, moist, and so on, and detailing their benefits and drawbacks, 'according to the advice of the surest ancient sources.'

This brings us to the four humors (dry, sharp, self-mocking, and sarcastic...?) Just as earthly bodies were believed to be composed of air, fire, water, and earth, the human body was seen as a composition of four fluids, which even today most people have heard of: blood, phlegm (or lymph), black bile and yellow bile. Each brings together two of the four fundamental qualities of heat and cold, dryness and moistness.

Making the matter more complicated—or more interesting, depending on your point of view—was the idea that each person, season, and stage of life is dominated by one of these, and each also correlates to personality, traits, tendencies, and foods which are good for individuals, depending on their dominant humor. (Bad puns certainly being one of them.)

Thus, a very simplified correlation of all this would be:

- Blood → Air (moist and hot) → childhood/spring → sanguine nature → pleasure → ruddy, vigorous, tends to gain weight → is drawn to meat with sauce, and wines
- Yellow bile (choler) → Fire (hot and dry) → youth/summer → choleric → yellow complexion, dry and nervous body → grilled meat, spices, hot and dry things
- Black bile → Earth (cold and dry) → adult/autumn → atrabilary/melancholic → grey complexion, thin → roots from the earth
- Phlegm/lymph → Water (cold and moist) → old age/winter → phlegmatic → pale, thin, and limp → soup, raw vegetables

The idea was to know one's humor and strive for balance within it. If things become unbalanced, it leads to physical and mental disturbances—that is, illness and madness. Medieval physicians therefore strove for balance among humors. This might include bleeding ad purging to remove excess fluid, or prescribing foods to improve the lacking humors and re-establish balance among them.

A Sense of Adventure

As I have delved more deeply into medieval food as a specific topic, I have come across a great deal of information that flies in the face of many of our current beliefs:

- Dogs were no more common at the dinner table then, than now.
- They were not as slovenly as they've often been depicted. In fact, it was typical to wash hands at the table before eating.
- Food was often well-spiced because they liked spices (as we do), not because the meat was rancid.
- Except times of famine, most people at well.

One thing interested me in particular, which dovetails with my study for another book I'm working on, *The Theology of Music*. In studying modes, and analyzing many dozens of medieval and modern songs, my co-author and I quickly saw that medieval musicians used a wide range of modes, whereas modern composers rarely branch beyond major and minor.

Similarly, in the world of cuisine, yes, much of what they ate would underwhelm the modern eater, and yet, the medieval diet was far more adventurous, varied—and whimsical—than what we enjoy. We would know and like much of what they ate. But they ate far more.

Our fowl consists largely of chicken and turkey, and occasionally duck, duck, or goose. (Gray duck, if you're in Minnesota). They, however, also ate starlings, gulls, herons, cormorants, grouse, pheasant, quail, cranes, peacocks, capons (castrated roosters, in case you're wondering—and castrating a rooster gives its meat a better flavor, also in case you're wondering)...and swans.

A sidebar story

The Feast of the Swan, is, in fact, a well-known historical event—at least, it's well known to medievalists, and, now, by you, unless you hastily avert your eyes from the following words! But there's no point in doing that. It's an interesting story. It occurred on Whitsunday, May 22, 1306, at Westminster Palace. It was at this great event that Edward II, age 22, was knighted by his aging father, Longshanks, aka Hammer of the Scots, aka Edward I, along with 267 other men.

This event ties directly to *The Blue Bells Chronicles* in that this great knighting ceremony was to gather a host to fight against Robert the Bruce, who would, eight years later, defeat Edward II at Bannockburn.

But we're getting ahead of ourselves.

80 minstrels were hired to play for this great event. That's important to an author who is also a minstrel, or, in modern terms, a musician. Several of them carried in a huge platter bearing two swans. (Yes, it was musicians who carried in the swans. And it was the band division that captured a German tank at the Battle of the Bulge—just saying.)

On these swans, oaths were sworn. Edward the Elder (who would not like to be known as such) swore to avenge the (purported) wrongs done him and England by that Scottish upstart Robert the Bruce (Edward's view, not mine) and then never more take up sword but in defense of the Holy Land. Eddie Junior (who would not like to be known as such), in turn, swore never to sleep twice in the same place, until he reached Scotland, that he might aid his father's battle.

The swans swore nothing. (Smart guys!)

As a sidebar story to the sidebar story, somewhat related to food —because it involves boiling—it was a year a a few months after the Feast of Swans that Edward the Aged arrived at the English side of the Solway Firth, Scotland before him across the water, and a massive army at his back, ready to take Scotland once and for all. Then he died. It was July 7, 1307 (a bit of an early birthday present for Robert the Bruce, who would turn 33 just 4 days later).

He commanded his son, Edward II, to boil his bones until the flesh fell away, and carry those bones at the front of the army that would conquer Scotland.

Ed Junior put Ed Senior in the grave complete and whole, flesh still on bones, and left those bones right where they belonged, on the occasions he ventured back to Scotland.

Hence, there will be no Potentate Pottage, no Sovereign Soup, and no Monarch Mulligan, among our historical recipes. I think that's for the best! It's one of the rare occasions on which I agree with Edward II.

Back to the variety of the medieval diet

We have a fair number of fish we eat: haddock, cod, salmon, sardines, oysters, and in some places, crayfish. They ate all these, and more: dogfish, porpoises, seals, whale, lamprey, and eels. We have historical recipes calling for perch, plaice, ray, minnows, barbels, mullet, bream, roach, trout, flounder, loach, salmon, sturgeon, haddock, codling, hake, milwell, tench, pike, dace, stockfish, luce, gurnard, porpoise, turbot, and lobster.

Among mammals, they ate not only beef (although their cows were smaller than ours) and pork, but hedgehogs, hare, venison, and wild boar.

We eat peas, various beans, carrots, onions, garlic (a root vegetable or herb, depending who you ask) and lettuce.   In addition to these (although the medieval carrot was a bit different from our modern version), they routinely ate turnips, parsnips,   leeks, chibols (spring onions), and a variety of lettuces and cabbages of many kinds.   One highly regarded cabbage in France, the cabbage of Senlis, produced an aroma more favorable than musk or amber, when its leaves opened. Now *that* is something I don't find at my local grocery store!

Their fruits consisted of apples, pears, cherries, plums, grapes, walnuts, damsons, gooseberries, strawberries, mulberries. Blackberries and sloes grew so profusely in the wild nobody bothered to grow them. This, to me, is evidence of their greater variety: how many of us have ever tasted a sloe, or even know what it is? They are the fruit of the blackthorn.

Their herb gardens, common in castles and monasteries, contained a variety of herbs used to season food.

They had porridges, stews, a variety of breads, and thick soups and stews known as pottage. They gathered berries and nuts—chestnuts, walnuts, pistachios, almonds, filberts, acorns, and pinenuts.

Granted, we have foods they didn't. We have orange carrots as compared to their purple, wild root vegetable. We have tomatoes, potatoes, corn, and turkey, all from the New World. They did not have yams, artichokes, green beans; red, green, or yellow peppers, or chilies. Pasta had not yet made its way over from Italy. Rice was rare.

Grapefruit—a hybrid of the Jamaican sweet orange and the Indonesian pomelo, is not recorded until 1750—approximately 25 to 50 years after the piano is believed to have been invented by Cristofori, who was employed by the Medici family, who was famous for poisoning people. Not that that train of thought reflects on my feelings about grapefruit. Not entirely.

I'm just saying—if you want an authentic medieval experience, don't eat grapefruit. And don't play the piano.

Called for in Many Medieval Recipes

To kick things off, here are a few ingredients frequently used in medieval cooking, which call for their own explanations or recipes.

Suet

Suet is unfamiliar to many modern Americans, but frequently called for in Scottish and medieval recipes. Suet is the hard white fat on the kidneys and loins of cattle, sheep, and other animals, used to make foods including puddings, pastry, and mincemeat. Mm, tasty!

It might take some looking, but can often be found at a butcher's, and sometimes even in the meat case at a grocery store. Most recipes that call for suet say *or lard.*

Verjuice

Verjuice was popular into the seventeenth century, and then seems to have largely disappeared. In recent years, it's having a bit of a 'rediscovery.' It was made from the juice of *not-yet-ripened* fruits or berries—grapes, sorrel, apples (especially in northwest Europe), gooseberries, or anything sour. And yet, the taste is described as not as sharp as vinegar, and it became more mild as it aged.

Due to the unripened ingredients, and its limited shelf life, verjuice was not reliably available all year long. In that case, we see that other things can be substituted: vinegar, (especially apple vinegar if you're going for northwest European versions of medieval recipes), gooseberry juice, lemon juice, and surprisingly, rose water.

Winter verjuice consists of *must,* which is fermenting grape juice, a very small amount of roasted salt, and unripe medlars, which are a fruit related to apples.

Summer verjuice, considered the 'emergency' version, was made of two thirds sorrel leaves and one third parsley ground together, then strained with wine and vinegar through a sieve.

The simplest method of making verjuice is this:

1. Wash unripened grapes well
2. Use the bottom of a jar to mash them well
3. Transfer them to a strainer (over a bowl) and use your hands to squeeze them, juicing them into the bowl
4. Put the resulting juice in bottles

The Eight Essential Spices

The following are frequently called for in medieval cooking:

1. Ceylon cinnamon (*cinnamomum zeylanicum*)
2. cubebs (*Piper cubeba*)
3. galingale or galangal (*Alpinia officinarum*)
4. grains of paradise (*Aframomum melegueta*)
5. hyssop (*Hyssopus officinalis*)
6. saffron (*Crocus sativus*)
7. savory (*genus Satureja*)
8. saunders/red sandalwood (*Pterocarpus santalinus*)

Galingale/Galangal

Whoever has pain in the heart area or is suffering weakness because of the heart, should immediately eat enough galangal and he will recover.
~ *Hildegard von Bingen*

Despite our notion that our medieval ancestors were uneducated and superstitious, there is growing medical evidence today that galangal does indeed stave off heart attacks.

Lumbard mustard

1. Roast 1/2 C. of mustard seeds, no more than 10 minutes, at 250 degrees F, then grind and put in a pot
2. Add 1/2 pt of white wine and 1/2 pt of honey
3. Bring slowly to a boil
4. Whisk an egg and add, whisking constantly
5. Remove from heat and add 2 tbsp of vinegar

Powder Douce

3 tbsp ginger
2 tbsp sugar
1-1/2 tbsp cinnamon

1 tsp cloves
1 tsp nutmeg

1. Mix together

That's it. Easy! Even a musician who depends on the microwave (not naming names!) could do it!

Powder Fort (Strong Powder)

Given that 'the middle ages' is a swath of time a thousand years wide and, even sticking to medieval Europe, still covering numerous countries and cultures, and given that recipes were much less likely to be written down, it's not surprising that there are multiple versions of *powder fort*.

Here are a few, although the key ingredients seem to be pepper and cloves, or, according to another source, pepper and either cinnamon or ginger. How's that for not terribly specific? That, however, is the fun of cooking.

Powder Fort 1

3 tbsp ginger	1 tsp cubebs
1 1/2 tbsp cinnamon	1 tsp grains of paradise
1 tsp cloves	1 tsp black pepper

For a modern reader, even these ingredients may require some explanation.

Grains of paradise are a peppery seed that comes from a plant in Africa. The name comes from medieval traders who claimed the seeds grew only in Eden and must be collected as they floated down rivers out of paradise. They are like pepper, with hints of flowers, coriander, and cardamom.

Cubebs are another peppery spice, a 'tailed pepper.'

Powder Fort 2

A second source gives these ingredients:

1 oz. pepper	1/8 oz. cloves
1 oz. cinnamon	1/4 oz. saffron
1 oz. ginger one of ginger	

Powder Fort 3

1/8 oz. cloves	2 oz. long pepper
2 oz. pepper	2 oz. nutmeg

1. Grind together

Almond Milk

Numerous medieval recipes call for almond milk. Here are several ways to make it.

Almond Milk 1

1-1/2 C. whole raw almonds   1-1/2 tbsp maple syrup or honey
4 C. water   a dash of cinnamon
1 tsp vanilla extract

1. Cover almonds with water and soak them 4 hours or more
2. Strain; add 1-1/2 cups of water; blend into a smooth paste
3. Add cinnamon and maple syrup or honey
4. Add remaining water; blend until smooth and frothy.
5. Strain through a strainer or cheesecloth to remove last almonds

Almond Milk 2

1/2 C. ground almonds   1 C. hot water
1/2 tsp clear honey

1. Dissolve honey in hot water and pour over ground almonds.
2. Steep 15 to 30 minutes, then train out almonds

Bonus: Almond Milk Butter

Botere of almand melk. Tak þikke almound melk & boyle it, & as it boyleth cast yn a litel wyn or vynegre, & þan do it on a caneuas & lat þe whey renne out. & þan gadere it vp with þyn hondes & hang it vp a myle wey, & ley it after in cold water, & serue it forth.
~ *Utilis Coquinario*

almond milk   cold water
red wine or red wine vinegar   heavy muslin OR fine strainer

1. Bring almond milk to a boil while adding wine or vinegar
2. Remove from heat and strain through heavy muslin
3. When liquid has drained, add remaining liquid to muslin sack
4. Leave in a cool place until liquid stops dripping, about 1-1/2 hours
5. Remove butter from cloth, divide into portions
6. Wrap each in cheesecloth; soak in cold water for several minutes

SAUCES

Scotland having a great deal of coastline, it's no surprise there are abundant meals of fish—and fish sauces often used in medieval recipes.

Galentyne, a strong sauce favored for pike and lamprey, was blended from white wine, vinegar, rye breadcrumbs and water and spiced with cinnamon, pepper and onion. Parsley sauce was served with saltwater fish—as we often do today. Cod with parsley sauce is still well known in England. Sauce verte, a green sauce, was made of fresh herbs, vinegar, and white breadcrumbs. It is one of the oldest medieval recipes that has come down to us. The *Viandier,* a French cookbook of the late 13th century, recommended it for boiled beef, pork, lamb, and especially for fish—pike, perch, bass, herring, carp, tench, bream, roach, chub, turbot, brill, and even conger eel.

Green sauce from *Liber Cure Cocorum*

Pur verde sawce.
Take persole, peletre an oyns, and grynde,
Take whyte bred myude by kynde,
Temper alle up with venegur or wyne,
Force hit with powder of peper fyne

Green Sauce from *Liber de Sent Sovi*

Finely chop, and grind: parsley, marjoram, sage, and mint. Add hazelnuts, walnuts, egg yolks, two cloves of garlic, toasted bread crumbs soaked in vinegar. Grind well, add dashes of oil and vinegar. Add honey or concentrated grape juice to taste.

Medieval Mint and Parsley Sauce

7 sprigs of fresh parsley	a small handful of breadcrumbs
5 sprigs of fresh mint	a pinch of salt
a tsp of garlic	a pinch of ground pepper
2 tbsp white wine vinegar	extra white wine vinegar

1. Soak breadcrumbs in vinegar for ten minutes
2. Chop parsley and mint finely, then grind garlic into them
3. Add breadcrumbs and herbs and blend until smooth
4. Add more white wine vinegar slowly, blending until smooth

And now...onto our gastronomic, historic, poetic, musical romp!

BLUE BELLS OF SCOTLAND

Blue Bells of Scotland begins the tale.

Shawn Kleiner is a modern classical musician, with the charisma and business sense to lift a small Midwestern orchestra to great heights. Auditioning for second, he is launched to principal, as his conductor enthuses, "He could turn a tin whistle into stardom!"

But Shawn also has a lot of personal problems. He is selfish and self-centered. He drinks, gambles, and cheats on his girlfriend. *Life is about having fun!* is his motto. Half the orchestra loves the skyrocketing incomes he's brought them. The rest are fed up with his antics. On their tour in Scotland, his girlfriend Amy has enough and abandons him in a medieval tower on a misty night.

Niall Campbell, a medieval Highlander, is everything Shawn isn't—responsible, devout, preparing to take on his duties as next Laird, if he survives the wilderness journey to raise troops for Bannockburn. His betrothed, Allene, demands to go with him. Angry, he spends the night in Glenmirril's tower on a misty night.

Shawn and Niall wake up in the wrong centuries, mistaken for one another. Shawn no longer has his money and fame to protect him from his many misdemeanors. Niall, caught in Shawn's life, learns his country and people are destroyed at Bannockburn. He must convince Amy to help him in his quest to change history.

What was Bannockburn?

It was Scotland's greatest victory, a true David and Goliath battle. In 1314, Robert the Bruce, having taken up the standard after the death of William Wallace, know to Americans as Braveheart, Robert the Bruce, King of Scots, led approximately 5,000 Scots against the might of England—20,000 heavy cavalry and infantry that stretched for miles and shook the earth as it passed, reports said.

While this book focuses on food, it is also a journey through this time in Scotland's history.

And so we step into *Food and Feast in the World of the Blue Bells Chronicles,* opening with Amy and Shawn having a picnic in the tower of Glenmirril. Glenmirril, sitting on the shore of Loch Ness, is modeled on Urquhart Castle, a medieval complex built in the 13th century, and captured in 1296 by Edward I. In 1298, it was once again controlled by Scots, and in 1303, by the English, held for Edward I by Alexander Comyn, kin to the Red Comyn whom Bruce would kill before the altar of Greyfriars Kirk just three years later in 1306. In 1307, Bruce marched through the Great Glen, taking back the castle of Inverlochy, Urquhart, and Inverness.

Glenmirril would be Urquhart's near neighbor, and the story is told among its people of the Glenmirril Miracle, a heavy mist which rose, protecting them from Edward I as he came through.

Before the current structure was built, Urquhart is believed to have been the site of the fortress of Brude, sometimes known as Bridei, the King of the Picts in the late 500s. St. Columba paid him a visit, converting him. More interesting to modern readers, perhaps, is the story, documented in Adomnan's *Vita Columbae.* Book Two of the *Vita, Of His Miraculous Powers,* tells how, in 565, Columba encountered a 'water beast.' It had killed one of the Picts, and attacked one of Columba's disciples. Columba banished it to the depths of the River Ness.

This is counted among his miracles, and also widely regarded as the first recorded encounter with the legendary Loch Ness monster.

Shawn and Amy's Picnic in the Tower

"...it just feels like-- like tension up here."

"Tension?" He looked around the tower. "Come on, you've read too many ghost stories about these old Scottish castles. What is it, the ghost of the woman who picked too many bluebells?" He laughed. "Let's eat. Roast beef? Boiled potatoes?" He settled himself on the flagstone floor, pulling plates and food from the basket.

Roast Beef Sandwiches

PREHEAT OVEN: 400 degrees F

1 can condensed French onion soup	1 tbsp of salt
1 tbsp Worcestershire sauce	6 tbsp red wine vinegar
3/4 lb thin-sliced roast beef	3/4 C. mayonnaise
4 hoagie rolls with sesame seeds	3/4 C. sour cream
4 slices provolone cheese, cut in half	1/2 tsp grated lemon zest
1/4 C. pickled banana pepper rings	tomatoes
1 red onion	watercress

1. Combine onion and salt, set aside for 20 minutes
2. Heat soup and Worcestershire sauce over medium high heat to a boil
3. Add beef, stirring occasionally; heat through
4. Rinse onion with cold water and drain
5. Marinate onions in vinegar, 30 minutes to 24 hours
6. Mix mayonnaise, sour cream, horseradish, zest, and 2 tsp of salt.
7. Add salt and pepper and hot sauce to taste
8. Place beef, cheese, and onions on each roll
9. Bake rolls on a baking sheet for 3 minutes (sandwiches should be toasted and cheese melted)
10. Spoon a little soup mixture onto each sandwich
11. Add mayonnaise mixture, tomatoes, watercress, and pepper rings

Boiled Potatoes

2 lbs fingerling potatoes
   or small new potatoes
1/4 C. lemon juice
1/3 C. extra virgin olive oil
1 tsp minced fresh thyme leaves
1 tsp minced fresh oregano leaves

1/2 tsp Dijon mustard
1 tsp salt
1/4 tsp pepper
1/2 red onion, thinly sliced
1/4 C. dry vermouth
1/4 C. chopped fresh parsley

1. Put potatoes in a pot with enough cold water to cover them by an inch
2. Bring to a boil, then add a little salt
3. Lower heat and simmer about 6-8 minutes, until potatoes are tender
4. While the potatoes boil, whisk together lemon juice, thyme, oregano, mustard, salt, pepper, olive oil
5. Add onion slices to this vinaigrette
6. Strain potatoes from water and put them in a bowl. Sprinkle with vermouth, and toss them to make sure all are coated with vermouth. Let sit for 1 minute
7. Add onions, parsley, and herb vinaigrette
8. Let sit for 10 minutes before serving

In the Great Hall with Iohn

At dinner, MacDonald had drifted off over his mead. Niall had gradually slowed Blue Bells of Scotland from the rousing battle tempo they'd been taking to a lullaby, encouraging the laird's nap. Guilt tickled his insides-- he had an idea why the poor man was so tired-- but mischief overtook him, and he changed the lyrics. Oh, where, and oh, where, he sang softly, Has my highland lairdy gone? A couple of ladies at the head table tittered, hands to mouths. "He's sleeping, he's sleeping, while his minstrel sings a song." More heads turned toward the unfortunate man. Niall sang a little louder. "He's drifted off to sleep, falling in his mead--" The laird's head lolled gently and came to rest atop his large pewter cup. A robust snore lifted from his slumbering form into the great hall. "And it's oh, how the ladies, laugh at his mead-covered cheek." Laughter swept across the hall. Allene, beside her father, met Niall's eyes. She tried hard to look stern. He wiggled his eyebrows at her. She covered her mouth and cast down her eyes. Iohn nudged him, and, with a wink, took over.

"Oh, where, and oh where, Has my highland lairdy gone? He's drifted, he's drifted off to the land of nod He's dreaming such sweet dreams Though his snores wake all the men, And it's oh, in my heart, I hope I can sleep again!"

The crowd burst into full blown laughter. The Laird bolted upright, wild-eyed and shaking his head. Droplets of mead flew from his beard. The crowd laughed harder. He looked suspiciously at Niall. "My lord!" Niall bowed deeply. "Why do you look at me so?" He took a long draught of his own mead, easing his aches. "Twas me singing," spoke Iohn. "My lord Niall is innocent." "This time," grumbled the laird. "Did I think otherwise, 'twould be another arrow he'd have in his arse!" The crowd roared. Niall rubbed his posterior and grimaced, bringing on more laughter. He winked at Allene, who blushed and lowered her eyes swiftly. "I sang your praises, my Lord," said Iohn. "You slept through it." The laird narrowed his eyes. The crowd held its breath. "My praises!" bellowed MacDonald, danger in his eye. "Aye, 'twould be very different praises you'd hae be singing had I been awake!" He wiped futilely at his beard and let out a big laugh. "Praises to my sweet smelling beard, aye!

> *"Wine can of their wits the wise beguile,*
> *Make the sage frolic, and the serious smile."*
> ~ *Homer*

Mead

From the Reynolds Historical Library's *Tractatus de Magnetate et Operationibus eius,* we get the oldest known surviving English mead recipe, from the 13th century.

ffor to make mede. Tak .i. galoun of fyne hony and to þat .4. galouns of water and hete þat water til it be as lengh þanne dissolue þe hony in þe water. thanne set hem ouer þe fier & let hem boyle and ever scomme it as longe as any filthe rysith þer on. and þanne tak it doun of þe fier and let it kole in oþer vesselle til it be as kold as melk whan it komith from þe koow. than tak drestis of þe fynest ale or elles berme and kast in to þe water & þe hony. and stere al wel to gedre but ferst loke er þu put þy berme in. that þe water with þe hony be put in a fayr stonde & þanne put in þy berme or elles þi drestis for þat is best & stere wel to gedre/ and ley straw or elles clothis a bowte þe vessel & a boue gif þe wedir be kolde and so let it stande .3. dayes & .3. nygthis gif þe wedir be kold And gif it be hoot wedir .i. day and .1. nyght is a nogh at þe fulle But ever after .i. hour or .2. at þe moste a say þer of and gif þu wilt have it swete tak it þe sonere from þe drestis & gif þu wilt have it scharpe let it stand þe lenger þer with. Thanne draw it from þe drestis as cler as þu may in to an oþer vessel clene & let it stonde .1. nyght or .2. & þanne draw it in to an oþer clene vessel & serve it forth

And gif þu wilt make mede eglyn. tak sauge .ysope. rosmaryne. Egre- moyne./ saxefrage. betayne./ centorye. lunarie/ hert- is tonge./ Tyme./ marubium album. herbe jon./ of eche of an handful gif þu make . 12. galouns and gif þu mak lesse tak þe less of herbis. and to .4. galouns of þi mater .i. galoun of drestis.

For the modern mead-maker, it would look like this:

1 gallon of honey   4 gallons of water

1. Heat the water.
2. Dissolve the honey into it
3. Let them boil, removing any foam that rises to the top
4. Remove from fire and let cool in another vessel
5. Transfer honey and water in a clean tub
6. Take lees from fine ale or yeast, add it to the honey/water and stir well
7. Lay straw or cloth around the vessel (insulate it). If cold weather, let stand for 3 days and 3 nights. In warm weather, 1 day and 1 night
8. For sweet mead, take the honey and water sooner from the lees; for sharper, let it stand longer
9. Draw it from the lees into yet another vessel and let stand another night or two
10. Draw it into yet another vessel and serve

Today, fermenters are used, and then as now, a variety of spices and herbs result in quite a wide selection of meads.

At the Medieval Market

The merry sounds of a festival reached out to him. He pushed himself, Brother David's abused body slamming into his back, his moans filling his ears, and reached the edge of the throng. Jugglers in harlequin clothing danced around him, spinning balls in the air. He gripped Brother David's legs, batting at the jugglers with his free hand, fought his way through to a booth laden with vegetables.

"Turnips, tasty turnips!" bawled an old woman, grabbing his sleeve. He spun his head, searching for Allene. Now there were more stalls, musicians strolling the street, a man with a monkey. He reached the outlying buildings of the town, his head twisting side to side, hunting for a hiding place.

"Your fortune for a penny," cried a scarved woman in front of a painted gypsy caravan.

"Breads, buns, rolls!" bellowed a fat man draped in white.

Shawn pushed through a gaggle of giggling children. Brother David grew heavier. Shawn's legs trembled under the weight. Stone houses and merchants' stalls rose around him.

"Fruits!" a young girl shrilled in his ear, snatching at his sleeve. "Five a penny!"

He took another step, twisted to peer down an alley for a hiding place. An acrobatic team strolled by on their hands, pointy shoes waving in his face. A boy led a string of ponies, brushing against him, making him stumble.

The smell of cheeses and fruits and meat and animals filled the air. Shawn spun, the weight of the monk on his shoulder growing; seeking sanctuary. People called and laughed. Colors spun in and out. His legs weakened under Brother David's weight. "Alms!" cried a toothless beggar, stretching a bony hand from among rags. His knee buckled. He grabbed a stone wall to steady himself. Something gripped his elbow. He spun, yanking his arm back,

Breads, Buns, Rolls

Bread-making has not changed much, although today we buy yeast from the grocery store, whereas our medieval counterparts used ale-barm —the froth that appeared at the top of fermenting ale, which was scraped off and used as the yeast to make bread.

As in everything, food differed by social class. Wheat flour was used to bake fine, white bread for the wealthier, while rye bread was more typically eaten by peasants.

I-Blessyd Be Cristes Sonde/ God Speed the Plough, 1450

The merthe of alle this londe
maketh the gode husbonde,
With erynge of his plowe.
I-blessyd be Cristes sonde,
that hath us sent in honde
merthe & ioye y-nowe.

The plowe goth mony a gate,
Bothe erly & eke late,
In wynter in the clay.
Aboute barly and whete,
That maketh men to swete,
God spede the plowe al day!

Browne, morel, & sore
Drawen the plowe ful sore,
Al in the morwenynge.
Rewarde hem therfore
With a shefe or more,
Alle in the evenynge.

Whan men bygyne to sowe,
fful wel here corne they knowe,
In the mounthe of May.
Howe ever Ianyuer blowe,
Whether hye or lowe,
God spede the plowe all way!

Whan men bygyneth to wede
The thystle fro the sede,
In somer whan they may;
God lete hem wel to spede
& longe gode lyfe to lede,
All that for plowemen pray.

erynge, plowing or preparing of the soil.
Cristes sonde, Christ's ordering of events.
In honde, here at hand.
gate, path.
eke, also
morwenynge, morning.

shefe, sheaf of grain.
here, their.
corne, wheat.
Ianyuer, January.
God lete hem wel to spede, let God give them good fortune

Fritter of Herbs

Frytour of erbes. Take gode erbys; grynde hem and medle hem with flour and water, & a lytel zest, and salt, and frye hem in oyle. And ete hem with clere honey.
~ *Forme of Cury*

good herbs (any kind you like!)	salt
flour	oil
water	honey
yeast	

1. Grind the herbs
2. Make a dough by mixing flour, water, a little yeast, and salt to a dough-like consistency
3. Mix in the herbs
4. Fry in oil
5. Drizzle with honey

Meat Pies

PREHEAT OVEN: 350 degrees F

1-1/2 lbs any combination: beef, pork, venison, rabbit, poultry

1-2 tbsp any combination of: ginger, allspice, cinnamon, nutmeg, cloves, cardamom, cubebs, galingale, etc.

1-2 C. any combination: minced dates, currants, raisins, minced figs, ground nuts

9" pie shell (lid optional)	1/4 tsp. salt
4 egg yolks	1/4 tsp. pepper
1/2-1 C. meat broth	grated cheese
splash of red or white wine	

1. Parboil, grind, or mash the meat
2. Mix all ingredients except chicken
3. Place in pie shell, cover with the lid and crimp edges to seal
4. Bake 45 to 60 minutes, until pastry is golden brown and filling sets
5. Serve hot or cold

Cider-poached Pears

6 pears	2 tsp ground ginger
2 tbsp honey	1 pt medium dry cider
dash of cinnamon	

1. Peel pears leaving the stem in
2. Combine honey, ginger, and cider in a pot and bring to a boil
3. Add pears; simmer 45 minutes, until pears are soft
4. Remove and serve

Sweet Treat, Bryndons

This is a 15th century recipe, but 14th century Scots no doubt had a similar treat.

Sauce:
- 1-1/2 pts cheap sweet red wine
- 1 C. diced figs
- 1-1/2 C. honey
- 1/2 C. red wine vinegar
- red food dye
- 1 tsp ground black pepper
- 1 tsp mace
- 5 cloves
- 1 tsp mace

- 1/2 C. chopped pitted dates
- 1/2 C. dried currants
- 1/2 C. pine nuts

Pastry:
- 4-1/2 C. wheat flour
- 2 C. sugar
- 1/4 tsp salt
- yellow food dye
- 1/2 C. water
- vegetable oil

1. Simmer figs in a little wine; set aside
2. In a separate pot, combine the rest of the wine with honey and bring to a boil, while skimming
3. Reduce heat and add vinegar, a few drops of red dye, pepper, mace, cloves, simmered figs, dates, currants, and pine nuts
4. Bring to a boil again
5. Leave to simmer, stirring occasionally
6. In a bowl, mix flour, sugar, and salt
7. Add a few drops of yellow food dye to water
8. Add colored water slowly to flour, forming a smooth dough
9. Roll dough onto floured surface
10. Cut into strips about 1 x 5 inches
11. Heat oil in a frying pan and fry strips to light golden brown
12. Set on a serving platter and cover with sauce

Cheese

Early History up to the Middle Ages

Most believe cheese was first made in the Middle East, the earliest type being little more than sour milk. We know the ancient Sumerians had cheese four thousand years before Christ, and we find mentions of cheese in the Old Testament. (*[They] brought...honey and curds and sheep and cheese from the herd, for David...to eat... 2 Samuel 17:28*)

The Romans excelled at cheesemaking, devising many flavors and characteristics in their *caseale,* or cheese kitchen. Their legionnaires took cheese as part of their rations, as they traveled the world.

In the Middle Ages, monks did a lot of experimenting with spices and herbs, creating many of the cheeses we know today—and it's surprising how many of our modern cheeses were known then—although as one historian has noted, that a cheese had the same name doesn't mean it was exactly like what we know today. Regardless, it is likely they were at least highly similar. The list of these cheeses known to medievals is quite long—and, sadly, probably quite boring, also. I thought I'd spice it up (see what I did there?) with some clever rhymes.

Beaufort, camembert, comté, and brie
all were known to the medievals and me

Emmenthal, maroilles, and cottage cheese
Mozzarella and gruyére are all bound to please
Today as in those past centuries

Okay, that was kind of...cheesy. Let's go back to the list, boring or otherwise:

Farmer's cheese is similar in both taste & texture to its medieval counterpart. Grana was first recorded in 1200 and gorgonzola all the way back in 879. They had port-salut, reblochon, ricotta, stilton, and Romano. We know roquefort was around by 1070.

Their rewen—also spelled rowen or ruayn—was made in the autumn and seems to have been a semi-soft cheese, although likely not as soft as a modern Brie, since one period recipe says to grate it. It might have been much like the modern French *fromage de gaing*. Medieval spermyse was another soft or cream cheese, flavored with herbs.

The first known records of cheddar date to 1500 (which is still quite a long time ago by our standards, but not quite as medieval as Niall), Parmesan in 1579, and Glouscester and gouda not until 1697.

The Medieval Process vs. Today's Process

I've chosen simple recipes that attempt to emulate the medieval process, and because I wanted readers to be able to make these without specialized equipment or ingredients like rennet or calcium chloride. The big difference between our cheesemaking and theirs is that our medieval ancestors could not go online to order bacteria cultures or rennet—an enzyme which aids in the process of cheesemaking.

So what did they do without that? They could get rennet from a calf's stomach. Most of this book's readers do not have calves. Well, not of the bovine kind, anyway. Rennet can also be made from thistles

1. Pick the head of the bull thistle flower (*cirsium vulgare*) when it has turned brown, before the plant starts producing thistle down. If there is any thistle down at all, the plant is unusable.
2. Dry the flower heads in a dehydrator or just in a sunny, airy place indoors.
3. When they are fully dried, remove the stamen—the purplish thread—from each flower.
4. Store these in a clean, dry jar with an airtight lid.
5. Grind two dried thistle heads with a mortar and pestle, into fine powder.
6. Repeat until you have 5 tsp of powder.
7. Put the powder in a bowl and pour warm water over it.
8. Soak for 5 to 10 minutes, watching for the liquid to turn dark brown.
9. Pour through a strainer to remove any last plant material.
10. Use one cup of thistle rennet per gallon of milk.

Thistle rennet should only be used in goat and sheep's milk cheeses. It will make cow's milk cheeses bitter, although bitterness can occur in any cheese made with vegetable rennet, if it's aged more than two months.

Posset

If we expect something exotic from medieval food, there are definitely times we will be disappointed. This particular 'recipe' calls simply for drizzling chunks of brie with honey and mustard mixed. A little more interesting is a cheese recipe from the *Harleian* manuscripts which uses ale to curdle the milk.

It advises we make a posset of milk and ale, draw the curds through a strainer with sweet white wine, 'somewhat running and somewhat standing, add sugar or honey, heat a little, & serve it, sprinkled with cinnamon, ginger, and perhaps white powder.

A posset is a drink made of hot milk curdled with ale, wine, or other liquor and (usually) flavored with spices. It is considered both a delicacy and a remedy for colds. That's my kind of cold medicine!

1 C. milk	dash of cinnamon
1/2 C. ale	dash of ginger powder
2 tbsp white wine or sherry	dash of white powder (cinnamon,
1/2 tsp honey	ginger, nutmeg and sugar mix)

1. Heat milk, then add ale and heat without stirring until it rises
2. Remove from heat and let cool completely
3. Strain liquid through cheesecloth; discard the liquid and save the curds
4. Strain the curds through a strainer into a small pot with the sweet wine or sherry
5. Add honey, warm, and pour into a bowl. Sprinkle with cinnamon and ginger

This sounds like a very liquidy cheese to me!

Basic Cheese with Salt

1 gallon *ultra pasteurized* milk, goat or cow
1 C. white vinegar
2 to 4 tsp sea salt

1. Put milk in a stainless pot, sprinkle in salt
2. Heat to 190 degrees F
3. Remove from heat and stir in vinegar, blending well.
4. Let sit for 20 to 30 minutes, checking to make sure it's well curdled
5. Pour this through a cheesecloth. Even better, put the cheesecloth in a strainer and pour the liquid through
6. Gather cheesecloth at the top and squeeze out as much liquid as possible
7. Hang the gathered cheesecloth and leave for 20 minutes to let as much liquid as possible drip out
8. When you open the cheesecloth, you will have cheese! Chill it in the refrigerator

This recipe can be easily adapted by stirring in herbs, chopped nuts, garlic, sun-dried and finely chopped tomatoes, roasted peppers, or really, just about anything, while it's still liquid.

In fact, the possibilities are almost endless, using spices and herbs. Dill and chives are favorites. For goat cheese, try thyme, olive oil, chives, and oregano and basil together. For brie, sage, rosemary, chives, or oregano are good. Oregano also blends well with soft cheeses, while thyme and sage are good for hard cheese. Fennel, garlic, and pepper are good in blue cheese.

Brother David and Allene Want to Kill a Deer

"How would you describe it, then?" asked Allene.

"Brutal," Shawn shot out. "Vicious and brutal."

"Certainly not!" Brother David sounded indignant. "We do not worship false gods like the pagans and druids. Nor do we offer human sacrifice or slaughter helpless babes, as did they."

"You kill people! You hit people. You stab people!" He stared pointedly at Allene, and wondered what had brought on those warm feelings toward her. Amy would never do that to him!

Allene gave an indignant toss of the head. "And this time you might come from? Did you dream about it in a delirium from your wound? Is it a time when men treat women like tramps to be pawed and groped, and force themselves upon them like enemy soldiers?" She pushed aside a branch and let it snap back in his face.

Shawn caught the branch, glared at her and fell silent, giving up hope of getting information. They followed a level track now, with ferns rising to waist height and spilling over the path. Birds sang from the treetops and undergrowth. A deer stood frozen in the underbrush, hoping not to be seen.

"Would I had a bow," Brother David sighed.

"'Twould be a fine meal," Allene agreed.

"See, this is what I mean," Shawn burst out.

The deer's head sprang up, alert to the gunshot of his voice in the still wood. It turned in one graceful motion and leapt, tail flashing white fear. Allene and Brother David sighed at the loss of their venison dinner.

"In this time I'm... I imagine... what if people were shocked by that?"

"By what? Eating a fine meal?" Allene pulled her sad gaze from the retreating deer.

"No, getting back to nature, seeing a deer, and the first thing you both want to do is kill it! What's up with that?"

"We're hungry," Brother David said. "Would it be wise in this time you imagine to starve rather than eat what God provides? Such a people would not long survive!"

Venison a la Bourguignonne

PREHEAT OVEN: 300 degrees F

2 lbs venison stew meat
2 C. red wine
1 bay leaf
1 onion stuck with 2 cloves
1 clove garlic, chopped
2 tsp thyme
2 tsp mustard
1 bunch of green onions, chopped
2-1/2 C. beef stock of bouillon

2 tsp salt
1 tsp black pepper
2 C. small whole onions
8 oz. mushrooms, sliced 1/4"
4 tbsp cornstarch
6 oz. thick slicked bacon
1 sprig of parsley

1. Fill a zip-lock bag with red wine, bay leaf, onion, and garlic
2. Add venison, seal, and marinate in a refrigerator for several hours
3. Remove venison, reserving marinade
4. Spray a frying pan with Pam and brown the venison over medium heat, stirring to avoid burning
5. Add green onions, herbs, spices, and enough stock to cover the meat and bring stock to a boil
6. Lower heat; cover pan and simmer for 2 hours
7. Fry bacon, drain, and chop into small pieces
8. After 2 hours, add onions and mushrooms to venison. Cook another 30 minutes
9. Add more salt, thyme, or mustard as desired
10. Mix cornstarch with cold water; pour slowly into the pan, stirring continuously
11. Serve with bacon bits

Venison Stew in Red Wine

2 lbs stewing venison, in 1" cubes	1 tbsp redcurrant jelly
2 bay leaves	1 C. cheap red wine
1 large chopped onion.	1 oz./quarter stick butter
1/4 C. flour	1-1/2 C. sliced mushrooms
	Salt and pepper

1. Marinate chopped venison in red wine and bay leaves for 48 hours
2. Strain out and save the wine; discard the bay leaves
3. Saute chopped onion in butter and oil for 10 minutes
4. Stir in flour and cook for another minute; add wine and stock
5. Boil, stirring until thick.
6. Stir in venison, redcurrant jelly and seasoning. Cover and boil another 5 minutes.
7. Reduce heat and simmer in a slow oven for about 4 hours or until tender.
8. Add mushrooms in the last 30 minutes

Shawn at Monadhliath

A table ran the length of the dining hall. The dozen brown-robed monks ate silently. Shawn's escort led him to an empty spot. He took his place, a red and blue peacock among sparrows. Someone set before him what must be the first course: a bowl of steaming stew, and a salad.

"Got some salad dressing?" he asked. "French?"

A dozen faces turned to him in shock.

Ah. Silence at mealtimes.

"Sorry," he muttered, and bent over the meal. The stew stared back at him, looking suspiciously like the evil twin of yesterday's meal at the castle. He watched as the monks reached into their bowls with their hands. Copying them, he fished out something like a scrap of potato with fingers less than clean after last night's doings. He continued eating, nonetheless, his hunger being greater than his aversion to sticking dirty fingers in his food. Still, the stew seemed less repulsive than it had at the castle; maybe because he was hungrier.

Barley Bread for Monks

We have a tendency, at least in modern America, to stick to our basic white and wheat breads. Medieval breads used a variety of grains. Barley was much more popular in medieval baking. This particular recipe also uses ale, which was used more often in baking and cooking —typically for meats or breads—then than it is today. Barley bread was a favorite of monks, for the health value of the barley. Given that they often also brewed beer, this may well be exactly what they ate.

The Rigs O' Barley by Robert Burns

It was upon a Lammas night
When corn rigs are bonnie
Beneath the moon's unclouded light
I held away to Annie
The time flew by wi' tentless heed
Till 'tween the late and early
Wi' sma' persuasion, she agreed
To see me thro' the barley
Corn rigs, an' barley rigs
An' corn rigs are bonnie
I'll ne'er forget that happy night,
Amang the rigs wi' Annie

Honey Barley Bread

PREHEAT OVEN: 450 degrees F

8 oz. barley flour

1 lb wholemeal flour

1 tsp salt

1/2 oz. fresh yeast, if thou hast no ale barm

2 tsp clear honey

1/3 C. brown ale

2 C. warm water

1. Combine flour and salt
2. Blend yeast with a little ale to make a creamy paste
3. Mix in the rest of the ale, honey, and 1-1/2 cups of warm water.
4. Add to flour and salt to make a firm dough. Add water carefully if you need to
5. Shape dough into a ball, set in bowl and cover. A modern recipe calls for clingfilm, but my guess is Shawn was not carrying clingfilm on him that night in the tower, and thus our medieval baker would have used a towel
6. Place the bowl in a warm area of the kitchen
7. Let it rise to twice its original size.
8. Remove the clingfilm (or the towel if you're a medieval baker who has gotten ahold of this book, but not clingfilm), press the dough down firmly and divide into two
9. Place each half in a bread or cake tin, cover each with a cloth and leave to rise again (sort of like Bonnie Prince Charlie—but not quite)
10. Bake about 20 minutes
11. Remove from oven, remove from tins, and cool on racks

Cabbage Pottage

1/4 tsp coriander or cardamom, ground

1 head of cabbage

3 C. of broth (chicken, beef, or vegetable)

2 onions

2 leeks

any other vegetable

1. Wash, chop, and slice the vegetables
2. Toss in a pot with stock
3. Bring to a boil
4. Lower heat and simmer 10 to 15 minutes

Medieval Salad with Herbs and Flowers

Salad was a little different, centuries ago, than what we know today. This is partly because some of the ingredients so common to our salads —tomatoes, potatoes, iceberg lettuce, red, yellow, and green peppers, for example—were not available in medieval Europe. Their salads included greens, like ours, but also herbs and flowers—yes, edible flowers! In some fancier grocery stores and upper end restaurants, flowers as food (or rather garnishes) are making a comeback, but it was more standard then.

Popular on salads were borage, fennel, purslane, garlic, mint, rosemary, and sage. Edible flowers included primroses, roses, and violets, while greens might include spinach.

Hildegard on Roses and Sage

Entire books could be written on the health benefits of all the possible ingredients of modern or medieval salads. And in fact, Hildegard von Bingen did. Well, she wrote a book on the benefits and drawbacks of numerous foods in particular. At the moment, we'll stick with just roses and sage as an example.

Remembering that medievals classified food by hot/cold and dry/moist, Hildegard labeled the rose *cold.* She recommended placing fresh-plucked rose petals on the eyes in the morning to 'draw out the humor' and make them clear. Rose petals placed on ulcers likewise drew mucus from them.

Rose and sage combined soothed wrath. A powder was made of rose petals and sage, and the powder held to the nose when one felt wrath rising. The sage soothes the anger, while the rose brings happiness.

Medieval Salad

7 C. baby spinach	1/2 C. walnuts
1 C. fresh mint leaves	1/2 C. fresh lemongrass, thinly sliced
1 C. diced prunes	1/2 C. violets, primroses, or any edible flower

1. Put it all in a bowl
2. Top with a light topping of oil and vinegar mixed together

Pottages

Pottage was perhaps the go-to meal of medievals. It consisted of...anything. Whatever happened to be available was thrown in a pot of water hanging over a fire, and stewed or boiled all day. Thus, pottage might be vegetable or meat. There were thin pottages, and there were thick pottages, called frumenty and morrews. These usually called for sugar, eggs, almonds, currants, and saffron, and thus, were more likely to be eaten by the upper class.

The following recipe, like so many then and now, is quite adaptable. The Monks, as we find out in later scenes have orchards and gardens. This soup may have been a base, to which they could have added anything from their garden—or even their orchard. In my research, I've come across a number of apple soups.

Oyle soppes

Take a good quantite of onyons, and myce hem, noyt to smale, & seth hem in faire water, And take hem vppe; and then take a good quantite of stale ale, as .iij. galons, And there-to take a pynte of goode oyle that is fraied, and cast the onyons there-to, And lete al boyle togidre a grete wile; and caste there-to Saffron and salt, And þen put brede, in maner of brewes, and cast the licour there-on, and serue hit forth hote.
~ Harleian Manuscripts

onions	saffron
ale that is flat, but not stale	salt
oil	day-old bread slice

1. Boil onions until partially cooked, then remove from water and leave to dry completely
2. Fry dried onions in hot oil until completely cooked and remove from oil
3. In a large pot, combine ale, onions, saffron, & salt; bring to a boil, then reduce heat
4. Simmer for 15 minutes to 30 minutes
5. Remove crust from bread and cut into strips
6. Place bread strips in the bottom of each soup bowl.
7. Spoon hot soup over the bread, then serve it forth!

Niall at the Two-Eyed Traitor

Niall stared thoughtfully at the letters on the menu, turned it right side up, and studied them again. Reading was easier than it had been. The spelling looked less like gibberish. But he wondered why Amy wished to read before eating. Their eyes darted uncomfortably at each other over the candlelight. A servant appeared with two crystal glasses of water sparkling on ice, each with a lemon floating in it.

Amy started reading again. Niall did likewise, making out venison and trout. The servant reappeared, hovering quietly with a sheaf of parchment and poised quill. "What are you having?" Amy asked.

"Having?" he repeated.

"It's a restaurant. What do you want?"

"I can—choose?" He had expected tables laden with repast, or a stream of servants bringing food as they did at the castle.

"Of course you can. You're paying." She smiled.

"A loaf of bread, then."

"A loaf, sir?" the servant asked.

"A whole loaf?" Amy repeated.

"Soup, eel."

"Eel? Did you say eel?" the servant asked. The black-suited man hurried over. He must be the steward, Niall decided.

"Where did you find that?" Amy searched her menu.

The servant looked to the steward, who nodded furiously.

"Pigeon pie, woodcock, salmon," Niall added, thinking of all his favorite things at the Laird's table. The waiter scribbled swiftly. Amy would certainly be pleased with him for providing this fine feast!

"Can't you make it easy and order off the menu?" Amy whispered, a little fiercely.

"Of course," Niall said obligingly. "Venison and trout would be good! And as we're celebrating, a boar's head!"

"A boar's head?" Amy said in disbelief.

"A... boar's head, sir?" The servant swallowed.

"Anything you like, Mr. Kleiner," the steward said loudly. He nudged the servant, who scribbled, frowning.

"Aye," Niall agreed cheerfully. "And plenty of ale!" At another table, a man handed his menu back to a servant. Niall did likewise.

"I'll have the chicken salad," Amy said.

*Our minds are like our stomachs; they are whetted by the change of
their food, and variety supplies both with fresh appetite.*
- *Marcus Fabius Quintilian*

Medieval History: Order of Serving Foods

Medieval feasts were quite an affair, with a wide number and
variety of dishes. Based on the belief that heavier foods would sink to
the bottom of the stomach and cause digestive problems. Therefore, the
lighter foods were served first. First, fruits, followed by soup, possibly
'pottage,' followed by meats. Lighter meats came first—first chicken,
then beef.

Lighter foods also followed these heavier foods. A meal would
conclude with a 'dragee,' perhaps of cheese or spicy wine, or small
pieces of sugared candies. We follow a similar pattern in our modern
day of appetizers, main course, and dessert.

Hearty Bread

PREHEAT OVEN: 375 degrees F

2 C. whole wheat flour   1 tsp baking soda
1 C. d all-purpose flour   1/2 tsp salt
1/2 C. rolled flour (divided)   3 tbsp melted butter
1 tsp baking powder   1-1/2 C. buttermilk

1. In a mixing bowl, combine whole wheat flour, bread flour, and
   1/4 cup of the rolled oats
2. Blend in baking powder, soda, salt, and butter
3. Make a hole in the center of the mixture and pour in buttermilk.
   Stir into a stiff dough
4. Sprinkle remaining 1/4 cup oats on bread board. Knead dough
   onto board for 1 minute, shaping it into a round loaf with the
   extra oats coated on the outside of the loaf.
5. Place loaf seam side down on a greased baking sheet.
6. With a knife, make a 1/2 inch deep cross slash in the top of the
   loaf
7. Bake 35 to 40 minutes, until the loaf sounds hollow when tapped.
8. Move to rack, brush with melted butter and cool 4 hours.

Pigeon Pie

PREHEAT OVEN: 355 degrees F

4 to 6 fledgling rooks*	Salt and pepper
1 lb beef chopped into 1" pieces	beef stock
6 oz. butter	Puff Pastry

1. Skin the rooks, removing the backbones and insides. Cut them into joints
2. Season the joints with salt and pepper and fry in hot butter until browned
3. Simmer the joints and beef in a pot of beef stock for two hours
4. Remove the rook meat from its bones. Save the stock for gravy.
5. Put beef and rook meat into a baking dish. Cover meat in melted butter and the remaining stock
6. Cover the dish with pastry
7. Bake for 30 minutes

Venison

3-1/2 oz. cold-pressed rapeseed oil	7 oz. soft dried figs
5 oz. balsamic vinegar	2 oz. port
4 small red onions, finely sliced	5 small red chilies
1 lb 12 oz. venison haunch steaks	

1. Heat half the rapeseed oil in a heavy frying pan
2. Add chilies and coat completely
3. Cook for about two minutes, until the skins begin to blister
4. Stir in red onions and cook for three minutes
5. Add venison steaks. Turn to seal all sides of the steaks
6. About 8 minutes will give you a medium rare steak
7. Add figs and remaining oil, followed by part and balsamic vinegar
8. Reduce for about three minutes

Trout

PREHEAT OVEN: 450 degrees F

4-1/2 lb trout	4 sprigs of fresh herbs
4 tbsp dry vermouth	—dill, fennel, chives, or parsley
2 tbsp olive oil	1 lemon
salt and pepper	

1. Trout: remove scales and fins and wipe with parchment paper—not the kind Niall would write on, though—the modern kind also known as kitchen paper
2. Season inside of trout with salt and pepper and put in herbs
3. Cut four pieces of tin foil into ovals three inches longer than fish. For the medieval cook, use cheesecloth soaked in clarified butter or rendered chicken fat
4. Brush this foil with olive oil (Speaking of rhyming cookbooks!)
5. Brush outside of the fish with olive oil—if you wish
6. No, seriously, really, I only got rhymes stuck in my head. Really, you must brush the outside of the fish with olive oil *and* season it with more salt and pepper, *and* pour a tbsp of vermouth over each fish
7. Pull foil up, wrapping fish and pinching it tight—what a sight!
8. Place on a baking dish (even if you don't wish); bake 8-10 minutes
9. Check that the fish is done—if there be no opaqueness or pinkness for trout, then you've won!

Eel Soup

1-1/4 lbs eels	1/2 tsp tarragon, chopped
2 oz. butter	4 oz. sliced onions
3 oz. flour	10 peppercorns
3 pints fish stock	3 blades of mace
1/2 tsp allspice	salt
2 tbsp parsley, chopped	5 fl. oz. sour cream

1. Soak the eels in salt and water.
2. Remove heads and tails and skins.
3. Cook the eles in melted butter, covered, for 10 minutes over low to medium heat. Do not brown. Remove the eels, set aside, and keep them warm.
4. Stir flour into the butter and gradually add fish stock.
5. Replace the eels and add herbs, onions, peppercorns, mace and salt.
6. Cook, covered, over low heat until the eels are tender
7. Strain, reserving the liquid as the soup.
8. Flake the fish off the bones and add the flaked eel back to the soup
9. Blend cream into the soup and heat through without boiling.

Eel

PREHEAT OVEN: 400 degrees F

2 lbs eel	1/8 tsp pepper
2 lbs lampreys	2 tbsp butter
1/4 C. flour	1/4 C. water
1/2 tsp salt	

1. Skin and clean eel and lamprey, split, and remove backbones
2. Cut fish in two or three inch pieces, wash in salt water, and dry thoroughly
3. Coat lightly with flour, season with salt and pepper, place in pan
4. Dot with butter
5. Add water to prevent burning
6. Cover and bake 15 minutes, until browned

Woodcock

PREHEAT OVEN: 400 degrees F

2 whole woodcock	1 sprig thyme
3-1/2 tbsp butter	1 clove garlic
3-1/2 oz. chicken livers	1 tbsp cognac

Rosti:

2 maris piper potatoes
3-1/2 tbsp butter, melted

Sauce:

3-1/2 oz. beef or game stock
3-1/2 oz. port
2 oz. smoked bacon, diced

1. Gut woodcock; set guts aside
2. Saute chicken livers and guts in butter, 1 minute on high
3. Add a few thyme leaves, salt and pepper and mix in a hand blender until smooth.
4. Impale the thighs of each woodcock with its own beak, brush with butter and sprinkle with thyme, salt and pepper.
5. Roast in the oven for 10 minutes, remove and set aside for 10 minutes.
6. Peel and grate the potatoes, add melted butter and season with salt and pepper
7. Fry in a non-stick pan on a medium heat, 5 minutes each side
8. Mix port and stock with bacon; cook on medium until thick.
9. Serve the woodcock on the rosti, and covered in the sauce

Salmon

Poaching Liquid:

5 oz. Scotch whisky	1 chopped carrot
2/3 C water	1 finely chopped onion
8 black peppercorns	3 tbsp lemon juice
3 bay leaves	1/2 tsp thyme
	Salt and pepper to taste

Whiskey Butter Sauce:

3 egg yolks	3 tbsp Scotch whisky
1 tbsp lemon juice	3 tbsp of poaching liquid
4 oz. butter	

1. Combine all the poaching liquid ingredients in a pan
2. Poach salmon 7-10 minutes or until fish is cooked
3. Strain and reserve the liquid
4. Set the salmon aside on a warm serving plate, covered to keep hot
5. Whisk egg yolks and lemon juice together in a heat-proof bowl
6. Place the bowl over a pan of hot but not boiling water on a very low heat.
7. Whisk until the mixture begins to thicken.
8. Stir butter in gradually, letting a little bit melt at a time. If lumps appear in the mixture, remove the bowl from the heat and add a tsp of cold water before placing back on the heat.
9. When all the butter has been mixed in and the sauce has reached a satisfactory thickness, remove from heat
10. Add three tbsp of whisky and three tbsp of poaching liquid.
11. Pour over the salmon and serve

Boar's Head

The boar's head in hand bear I
Bedecked with bays and rosemary
And I pray you, my masters, be merry
Quot estis in convivio

Caput apri defero
Reddens laudes Domino

The boar's head, as I understand
Is the rarest dish in all the land
Which thus bedecked with a gay garland
Let us servire cantico

Caput apri defero
Reddens laudes Domino

Our steward hath provided this
In honor of the King of Bliss
Which, on this day to be served is
In Reginensi atrio

Caput apri defero
Reddens laudes Domino

History

The wild boar, in addition to having a place in the legends and myths of several countries, is one of the most vicious animals and one of the most fearsome to hunt. (Niall will encounter one many months from his dinner at the Two-Eyed Traitor.) The boar's head was a major part of feasts, especially the Christmas feast, among the wealthy. This tradition dates back to pagan times, and some say also to Rome. It had a place in the Celtic and Norse worlds, in addition to medieval Britain. In Swedish art, St. Stephan is seen tending horses and bringing a boar's head to the Yuletide feast.

It would take days to prepare it, and its entrance was an event. It was brought in on a huge gold or silver dish, generally garnished with rosemary and bay, often with apples, almonds, and raisins, and accompanied by the sound of trumpets and a procession of minstrels and servants and sometimes the men who took part in the hunt. The presentation of the boar's head on Christmas Day came to represent the triumph of the Christ, with his birth, over sin.

Where to buy it

Buying a boar's head can be tricky. You may find one at a butcher shop, or you may need to buy an entire boar (or pig, as is commonly used today) from a small farm, or find a butcher who can order one for you. They tend to be fairly economical (or, as we say here in my house, cheap) due to low demand. (Funny, that! But I wonder how my kids feel about boar's head for dinner tonight. Actually, that won't work. It can take some time to acquire one, due to usually having to order through a butcher.)

Heads come whole, or cut in half. The whole head will look more impressive, but will take longer to cook and is more difficult to serve.

Boar's Head 1

THE DAY BEFORE THE FEAST: *Clean it:*

Remove long hairs, including eyelashes. Tools for doing so range from a disposable razor to a blowtorch. I, personally, have a firm rule against blowtorches when my boys are cooking. I try to remember to simply be grateful that they like to cook at all, but I still have my limits. It's okay if some hair is still visible under the skin.

Brine it:
1. Brining removes remaining blood, and gives flavor to the meat.
2. A good brine requires: time, salt, cold
3. Use ice water and1 cup salt for every gallon of water: ice counts as water!
4. Dissolve salt into the smallest possible amount of water and cool it down before using it
5. Sprinkle in parsley, sage, thyme, and several shallots
6. Let the boar's head brine for 12 to 24 hours. Longer is better.

THE DAY OF THE FEAST: *Cook it:* Low and slow is the key!

aluminum foil	salt
2 meat thermometers	maple syrup
oven thermometer	2 very large flippers
meat brush	A very large tray

PREHEAT OVEN: 250 to 275 degrees F
OR: LOW TO MODERATE ON ONE SIDE OF BARBECUE

1. Put oven thermometer on the unlit side, close to the lit side temperature on unlit side should be 250 to 275. Check temperature throughout cooking
2. Season meat heavily with salt
3. Put tin foil 'tents' on the ears, not too far down
4. Place head on the grill (or in oven) skin side up if it's in halves
5. As the temperature nears 170, baste head with maple syrup. Do this 4 or 5 times in the last couple of hours of cooking
6. Cook 6 to 10 hours to a temperature of 170 F
7. Remove from the oven or barbecue.
8. Tent head in tin foil until it's time to serve

Boar's Head 2

A French version of the boar's head recipe recommends singing the head (there's that blowtorch again!) and scrubbing it with a brick (sounds a little safer) to remove the hair. This (and other recipes) call for removing jawbones and snout, brain and tongue, rubbing salt into all the parts of the flesh, and putting the head together again.

In this version, we wrap and tie the head in a cloth, boil it with leaf-fat of a pig, bay leaves, lots of sweet herbs (unspecified), coriander, aniseed, salt, nutmeg, ground cloves pounded, rosemary, and anonion. When half boiled add a quart of wine—yes, this sounds very good! I think Niall would like this, too!

Now, let it boil for twelve hours. When fully boiled, let it cool in its own liquor. Serve cold.

Boar's Head 3

A third recipes adds two stuffings. The first is of minced pig's liver, chopped apples, onion, sage and rosemary, arranged half an inch thick inside of the head.

The second, which fills the rest of the head, consists of sausage meat, ox tongue (mm, mm good!) truffles, apples, mushrooms, pistachio nuts, minced rosemary, a wineglass of Calvados (or sherry) and one of cream.

This, too, is boiled 8 to 9 hours, after which it is 'reshaped in cloth,' and allowed to cool. The ears, removed and boiled separately, will be re-attached to the head with a skewer. It will all be served on a dish with slices of truffles and apples and sprinkled with rosemary.

Boar's Head by Sabina Welserin, 1553

Sabina Welserin, a young woman of the 1500s, boiled her boar's head in water, and when it was done, basted it with wine. She made either a black or a yellow sauce. The black sauce consisted of browning a spoonful of wheat flour in heated fat, and adding to that good wine, cherry syrup, sugar, ginger, pepper, cloves, cinnamon, grapes, raisins, and finely chopped almonds. "Taste it," she concludes, and, "however it seems good to you, make it so."

The yellow sauce is made the same way, except that saffron is used in place of cherry syrup, and no cloves are used.

Book Two: THE MINSTREL BOY

History

The Minstrel Boy begins in the days immediately after Bannockburn.

The battle should, in theory, have gone to Edward II. He commanded a force of roughly 20,000 to 30,000. Reports say it was the biggest army raised in years, and that it stretched for twenty miles down the road, with knights on mighty warhorses, thousands upon thousands of infantry, and the wagon train.

Bruce, by contrast, had a small band of Scots, by some estimates as low as 5,000. They had fewer cavalry, and what their cavalry rode was not great warhorses, but smaller animals (now extinct) called garrons—more like our modern ponies.

Despite this, Bruce won. He did so by:

- Choosing the land well—swampy, damp land on which England's heavy horses could not fight well, and an area hemmed in by river and stream, such that Edward could not adequately use his vast host
- Preparing it ahead of time with murder pits and caltrops—spikes that pierce a horse's hooves and bring it down
- And, some would say, by the hand of God, as he prayed for the intercession of Saints Fillan and Columba, and had the blind old Abbot of Inchaffray say Mass the morning of battle, and bless and absolve his men

Thus, *The Minstrel Boy* begins with rejoicing and feasting at Stirling Castle in celebration of the improbably victory.

Niall Receives His Father's Sword

On a stool before the great head table, surrounded by long trestle tables teeming with hundreds of knights who had fought at Bannockburn, Niall plucked his harp, harmonizing as he sang the *Falkirk Lament* in tribute to those who had fallen in battle, who were not here to share the feast.

With his eyes closed, Niall saw not the great hall of the medieval castle, not the platters of roast and venison and serving boys rushing with food, but the great concert hall half a country and seven centuries away, where he'd last played the Lament, not the tapestries on the castle walls, but the curtains soaring to a ceiling high above; not the fires blazing in the hearths, but blinding electric spotlights.

He heard not the shouts and laughter of victorious knights, but the swell of a hundred musicians, trumpets and flutes and nasally oboes all backing the plaintive lament, Amy's violin singing sweetly behind him, and the thundering applause of a crowd as big as Bruce's entire army. Shawn played on the edges of his mind. They had thought it was Shawn they applauded. His fingers drifted up the last arpeggio, and became still, letting the notes shimmer in the air, missing that concert stage seven centuries away.

He opened his eyes, disoriented at seeing the great hall around him, the sconces and surcoats and wolfhounds and weapons. The sweet scent of rushes mingled with the tantalizing odors of meats, vegetables, breads, and ales. Men jostled at the tables, eating, drinking, and roaring with laughter and talk.

At the head table, piled high with roasted boar and glazed fowl, sat Robert the Bruce, King of Scots, surrounded by his brother and his earls. A thin crown of gold circled his graying auburn hair. Sunlight, strong even late in the evening, shone through the windows of the hall and glinted off the rearing lion, picked out in thread of gold, on his tabard. He leaned back, looking pleased.

Several seats down from him, beside her father, Allene beamed with pride. Niall smiled at her.

Bruce rose from his seat. A hush came over the great crowd.

Tearing his eyes from Allene, Niall scrambled to his feet, surprised.

Like a master musician, Bruce let the silence hang, looking around the room, meeting half a dozen eyes, before lifting his chin. "Niall of Glenmirril, come forward."

Music is the wine which inspires one to new generative processes, and I am Bacchus who presses out this glorious wine for mankind and makes them spiritually drunken.
~ Ludwig van Beethoven

a douce egre (sweet and sour fish)

A dauce egre. Tak luces or tenches or fresch haddok, & seth hem & frye hem in oyle doliue. & þan tak vynegre & þe thridde part sugre & onyounnes smal myced, & boyle alle togedere, & maces & clowes & quybibes. & ley þe fisch in disches & hyld þe sew aboue & serue it forth.
~ Utilis Coquinario, 14th century

luces, tenches, or haddock	1 onions
olive oil	1/4 tsp mace
2 C. vinegar	1/4 tsp cloves
2/3 C. sugar	1/4 tsp cubeb
a little water	

1. Put fish in a baking pan with enough water to almost cover it
2. Bake through, then remove from pan and drain
3. Combine vinegar, sugar, onion, and spices in a pan
4. Bring to a boil, then reduce to a simmer
5. Cook until onions are soft
6. Fry fish in oil until outside is crispy; drain oil, serve with sauce

Venison from Liber Cure Cocorum

Roo in a Sewe.
Take þo roo, pyke hit clene forthy;
Boyle hit þou shalt and after hit drye;
Hew hit on gobettis, þat ben smalle,
Do hit in pot withalle;
Kest wyn þerto, if þou do ry3t,
Take persole and sawge and ysope bry3t,
Wasshe hom and hew hom wondur smalle,
And do þerto hit þou schalle,
Coloure hit with blode or sawnders
~ Liber cure cocorum

For stuffed pigs

For pygges farsyd.
Take swongen eyrene and floure þer to,
And powder of peper er þou more do;
Blend alle togeder and salt þerwith;
Coloure hit with safrone, so have þou blythe;
Put alle in body of þo pygge,
Rost hit on broche of irne bygge
Enfarsed; þo cle of pygge schalle be
Festened in þe cheke so mot þou þe;
Þo hender legges enoynt þou schalle,
Þo cles by þo sydes þou festun withalle
~ Liber cure cocorum

Mashed Peas

2 sprigs parsley
5 mint or hyssop leaves
2 sage leaves
4 small savory leaves

2 lbs fresh green peas
[1 lb if using frozen peas]
1 C. broth, chicken, beef, or vegetable
1 slice of bread, crumbled

1. Boil peas in broth until almost cooked—10-12 minutes
2. Put some of the broth into a separate pan
3. Mash herbs and breadcrumbs into it with a wooden spoon
4. Add half the cooked peas, mash them into a thick sauce
5. Drain the remaining peas and add them to the sauce
6. Reheat and serve hot

For frozen peas, half the amount
For dried herbs: mint or hyssop 1/2 tsp   dried sage 1/4 tsp   dried savory 1/4 tsp

Chyches (Roasted chickpeas with garlic and oil)

Chyches. Take chiches and wrye hem in askes al nyght oþer al a day, oþer lay hem in hoot aymers. At morowe waische hem in clene water, and do hem ouere the fire with clene water. Seeþ hem vp and do þerto oyle, garlek hole, safroun, powdour fort and salt; seeþ it and messe it forth.

~ *Forme of Cury, 14ᵗʰ century*

Elderflower Chicken

A number of flowers are edible, and were used for their medicinal properties. Elderflower is an antiseptic, a laxative, an anti-inflammatory, and good for the complexion to boot! But they were also popular in medieval cooking. You'll find many recipes that use elderflowers: jams, teas, vinegars, and more.

7 elderflower clusters	4 egg yolks
4 oz. ground almonds	1 tsp salt
2 lbs chicken breasts	

1. Poach chicken in salted water 30-40 minutes until tender
2. Strain broth from chicken breasts, saving 2 cups
3. Remove skin from chicken and set aside, keeping warm
4. Steep almonds in the 2 cups of strained broth for 20 minutes
5. Strain ground almonds from mixture, leaving almond milk
6. Grind salt and elderflowers together and stir into the almond milk
7. Pour sauce over chicken and serve

NOTE: When preparing elderflowers, strip the flowers entirely from their stems. Use *only* the flowers, no stems at all.

Funges (Mushrooms in broth and spices)

*Take funges and pare hem clene, and dyce hem; take leke and shrede
hym small, and do hym to seeþ in gode broth. Colour it with safroun,
and do þerinne powdour fort.*
~ Forme of Cury, 14th century

Powder fort is a mixture of ground spices, usually including pepper
and/or cloves. How's that for quite non-specific?

4 C. broth	1/2 tsp cloves
2-1/2 C. sliced mushrooms	1/2 tsp pepper
1 large onion	a pinch of saffron
1 C. of sliced leeks	

Good Broth:

3 C. chicken broth	1/2 tsp. each pepper & cumin
1 C. pork broth	pinch of saffron
1/2 – 1 C. bread crumbs	salt (to taste)

1. Bring combined broths to a boil
2. Add bread crumbs Imore for thicker sauce) and spices
3. Return to a boil
4. Reduce heat and cook for a minute
5. Remove from heat: use now or refrigerate for later

AND NOW:

1. Put mushrooms, onions, leeks, and broth in a pot
2. Bring to a boil
3. Reduce to a simmer and add spices

Fruits in Wine/Dessert

Pears poached in red wine, sometimes with other fruits, was a popular banquet dish.   They were often mixed with other fruit—mulberries being a favorite—and invariably with ginger and cinnamon. *Wardonys in syrup* was one such dish:

pears	ginger
red wine	touch of saffron
sugar	a very little ginger
cinnamon	

1. Put all ingredients in a pot
2. Bring to a boil
3. And that favorite medieval conclusion: mess it forth! Or serve it forth if you're feeling particularly neat today!

Glazed Fowl

The 14th century *Le Viandier de Taillevent* describes this dish, reminding us not to plump the birds, and to push straw between the skin and flesh. Do not damage the skin!

PREHEAT OVEN: 350 degrees F

1 chicken, feet and head still attached
1 lb mutton, veal, and/or
    dark chicken meat
6 eggs, beaten
1/2 C. cooked chestnuts
1 C. mozzarella or brie
1/2 – 1 tsp black and white pepper

1/2 to 1 tsp savory
1/2 to 1 tsp cumin
a few threads of saffron
1/2 tsp. salt (or to taste)
2 egg yolks
yellow & green food dye
unseasoned bread crumbs

1. Cook and dice meat; dice or shred cheese
2. Combine everything except chicken in a large bowl; mix well
3. Stuff chicken with this mixture, reserving leftover stuffing
4. Rub olive oil on chicken; set belly-down on foil-lined baking sheet
5. Sprinkle with salt & pepper
6. Wrap feet, head, and wings in foil
7. Bake until skin begins to turn golden brown
8. Dye egg yolks, some in gold, some in green
9. Remove fowl from oven; remove foil
10. Paint chicken with egg yolk—have fun!
11. Return to oven just a few seconds; leaving it in too long will ruin the colors!
12. Remove from oven, place on a serving platter
13. Garnish with 'eggs' made from leftover stuffing

Stuffing eggs:

1. Shape remaining stuffing into 'eggs.' If stuffing is too moist to do so, add bread crumbs until it holds together
2. Bake eggs on a well greased sheet and bake at 350° F for 1/2 hour
3. Brush eggs with colored yolk; return briefly to oven to set glaze. When ready, place along side the hen on its serving platter.

Walnuts make a suitable substitution for the chestnuts, an ingredient often not readily available.

Subtleties

As stated earlier, my research has led me to wonder if medievals, contrary to our modern view, didn't have a greater and wider experience and creativity than we do. They used a greater variety of musical modes. One has only to look at their architecture to see the beauty woven in, compared to our impressive, but stark sky scrapers and, especially, our utilitarian modern office blocks. They dined on a wide variety of food.

And then there's the matter of 'subtleties.' These were a favorite at feasts, unlike anything we know today. They were whimsical, colorful, culinary flights of fancy: birds within birds, hedgehogs, four and twenty blackbirds baked in a pie, chickens that appeared ready to eat, only to suddenly come to life and scamper across the table, foods that arrived at the table and began singing, the cockentrice—created animals.

It is easy to picture the imaginations of the medieval cooks working overtime, thinking up surprises, and equally, the delight and amazement of the medieval dinner guests, seeing these things for the first time. What is there in our own time that gives us a similar delight and amazement, the unexpected that takes us by surprise, and leaves us laughing?

For a feast in the presence of the king, in the wake of a great victory, I think we can safely assume a rather fantastic subtlety or two.

Singing Swans

There is a remarkable thing about swans. They teach us that the troubles of death should not grieve us; for in the very moment of dying they make a virtue of necessity and despise their sad fate in singing.
~ Gerald of Wales, c. 1145-1223

For such an event, singing swans and fire breathing roasts are hardly too much! The *Viviender* tells us how it was done in the 1400s.

Fine poultry for a king: quicksilver
Swan, goose, duck, chicken   ground sulphur

1. Prepare, cook, and dress poultry and arrange on a platter
2. Tie the bird's neck, then fill with quicksilver and ground sulphur
3. Reheat and serve to the delight of king and crowd!

Fire Breathing Roasts

boar's head, piglet, swan, fish,   cotton
    OR any animal!   alcohol

1. Combine cotton and alcohol, presumably in the animal's mouth
2. Light them!

Amy's Stir Fry

With vegetables and beef sizzling on the stove, with nothing left to put it off, with shaking hands, Amy called Carol. The phone rang. She hoped Carol wouldn't answer. But it clicked, setting her nerves jangling. She gripped the phone in one hand, and Niall's crucifix in the other.

"Amy." Carol's voice sounded ragged and thin. But warm.

"Carol. Hi." Amy drew in a breath. The crucifix bit into her palm. "I'm sorry I didn't call sooner."

"Oh, Amy, don't apologize," Carol said. "You're dealing with a lot. You must be hurting, too."

Typical of Carol, Amy thought, thinking of someone else even in her own distress. Her hand relaxed on the crucifix. There was no need to admit she'd broken up with Shawn. She almost confessed, *I left him there*. But the world thought he'd disappeared later, at the re-enactment. Besides, she *was* hurting. "I'm...okay," she said.

"Are they still looking for him?" Hope fluttered in Carol's voice. "Is that why you stayed?"

"Uh, yes." Amy sprinkled seasonings on the stir fry. She couldn't tell Carol her son was dead, could only leave her hanging in limbo, praying and waiting for news Amy alone knew would never come. She set the spice bottle down hard, asking herself again what she expected from her rash decision to stay. But she felt at peace being near Shawn and Niall—even if they were both dead.

Stir Fry with vegetables and beef and seasonings

1 beef bullion cube
1/3 C. boiling water
2 tbsp soy sauce
2 tbsp cornstarch
1 tbsp teriyaki sauce
2 tsp white sugar
3 tsp of garlic
1 tbsp of minced ginger

1 tsp of sesame oil
1 lb beef round steak, in thin strips
1 tbsp olive oil
1 C. pea pods
2 thinly sliced carrots
1 thinly sliced onion
1 thinly sliced red pepper
4 oz. can sliced water chestnuts

1. Dissolve beef bouillon cube in boiling water
2. Stir in soy sauce, cornstarch, teriyaki, and sugar
3. Marinate beef strips in teriyaki, coating well
4. Use half the oil to coat pan, heating for 30 seconds.
5. Stir-fry beef; set aside
6. Add remaining oil to wok; stir-fry garlic and ginger 10 seconds
7. Add red pepper; stir-fry 1 minute.
8. Add onions; stir-fry 30 seconds
9. Cover and steam 2 minutes
10. Return beef to wok, but push beef and vegetables to side
11. Pour soy mixture in middle; stir 1 to 2 minutes until thickened
12. Stir vegetables and beef in sauce until glazed and coated
13. Sprinkle in cashews; remove to serving dish

Rose and Amy have Lunch

When the taxi had dropped them at the pub, Rose pulled dozens of brochures from her straw purse and spread them over the table, taking Amy on a dizzying potential itinerary that left her almost as exhausted as if they'd actually visited each of the places. Amy was grateful when the waitress appeared with fish pie, coffee, and a glass of wine for Rose. Gathering the brochures, Rose flashed a smile. "Thank you, dear! It looks delicious! What's the best place in Scotland?   What should I absolutely not miss?"

"Inverness," the waitress said promptly.   "Shopping, theater, hiking, boating, anything you want."

"Inverness it is," Rose announced. "Thank you!" She turned to Amy as the waitress left. "Shall we take a bus or train?"

Amy picked up her fork. "You never run out of energy, do you?"

"Nope, and I don't intend to." Rose sipped her wine. "Glenmirril's in Inverness, isn't it?"

"You want to see Glenmirril?" Amy lowered her fork.

Miss Rose set her wine down. "That traumatic? What happened there, Amy?"

Amy stared at her fish pie. "I left him."

"You justifiably walked away. He's a grown man. Why didn't he follow you out of that tower?"

"He wanted to finish his picnic."

"His choice. He could have called a cab."

"His jacket was in the car," Amy said, "with his cell phone and money."

Rose sniffed. "He could have walked home. But what I want to know, Amy, is, *what happened* in that tower that upsets you so much?"

Amy pushed at the fish with her fork. "What did the news say?"

"That he was injured, had a fever and behaved strangely afterward, and then disappeared."

"That's about right."

"Amy, why won't you look at me? How was he injured?"

"An arrow," she mumbled.

"Like a bow and arrow?" Rose asked incredulously.

Amy lifted her eyes. "Rose, the news didn't say everything, because they don't know everything. It wasn't Shawn who left the tower with an arrow wound and a fever."

Fish Pie

PREHEAT OVEN: 400 degrees F

Topping:
   sea salt
   ground pepper
   2 lbs of potatoes

Pie:

1 medium carrot	10 oz. salmon fillets, skinless
2 celery sticks	10 oz. haddock or cod
5 oz. cheddar cheese	4 oz. prawns or shrimp
1 lemon	olive oil
half a fresh red chili or a jalapeno	1/2 C. spinach
4 sprigs of fresh parsley	2 tomatoes, quartered

1. Bring salted water to a boil
2. Peel potatoes and cut into chunks.
3. Add to boiling water; cook until soft
4. Peel carrot into a deep baking dish
5. Grate celery, carrot, and cheese into the baking dish
6. Grate the zest from a lemon on the fine side of a grater, into the baking dish
7. Finely grate chili into baking dish
8. Finely chop parsley leaves and stalks into baking dish
9. Cut salmon and haddock into bite-size pieces, mix with prawns
10. Squeeze juice from zested lemons over fish
11. Drizzle with oil; sprinkle with salt and pepper
12. Add spinach and tomatoes and mix everything together well
13. Drain potatoes and return to pan
14. Drizzle potatoes with olive oil and sprinkle with salt and pepper, and mash until smooth
15. Spread over top of the fish and grated vegetables
16. Bake 40 minutes, until cooked through, crispy and golden on top

Niall and Shawn Practice Fighting

They worked while the sun climbed high in the sky, till Shawn's muscles screamed in pain, till sweat ran down his back under the padded gambeson, till his mouth was dry as sandpaper, and a headache throbbed in his temples, till he vowed he'd take the wooden sword to Niall as soon as he had the strength to swing it. They worked to the sound of men and horses racing at quintains across the field. Finally, with the sun blazing directly overhead, Hugh approached, swinging a leather bag.

"Dinner." Niall grinned, lowering his sword. "And I daresay some ale."

"I daresay it's high time." Shawn tugged his helmet off. Light and air and a full range of vision had never felt so good. "You people have a startling lack of awareness of the dangers of *dehydration*." He used English where there was no Gaelic.

"What's that?" Niall asked.

"Lack of water."

"Aye, well, we're not given water breaks in battle, are we?" Niall hailed Hugh. The giant of a man tossed the sack the last couple of feet, and Niall caught it easily.

"Progress?" Hugh asked.

"Barely."

"I object!" Shawn flung down his sword. "I scared off that crow!"

"No, it was flying home to get its friends to come and laugh at you, too." Niall chuckled, pulled out a bundle of bannocks wrapped in a kerchief, and tossed a couple to Shawn. He wolfed them down. Hugh took a long draft of ale from the skin he carried, before passing it on.

Shawn hesitated only a moment before deciding he'd risk germs over dehydration. The ale slid down his throat cold and wet and more glorious than anything he'd ever drunk. His irritation with Niall slid away as quickly. A broad grin covered his face. "Whew, that's good!" he shouted. "What do you guys put in this stuff?"

"Hard physical labor," Niall said dryly.

"It makes everything taste better," Hugh added. "After you eat, Allene's ready to work with him on his script and Latin."

"*Veni, vidi, vici,*" Shawn muttered. "*Carpe diem.* Fish today."

Hugh shook his head and walked away

Bannocks

An option is to use butter and sweet milk instead of buttermilk.
Originally from F. Marian MacNeil's *The Scots' Kitchen*

3 C. fine oatmeal   1/4 tsp salt
1/2 C. plain flour   1/4 pt of buttermilk

1. Preheat your girdle if you are a medieval Scot (or cook like one) or your pan if that's what you have. Sprinkle flour on it—if it takes a few seconds to brown, your girdle/pan is hot enough
2. Mix oatmeal, flour and salt in a large bowl
3. Mix buttermilk briskly in a small bowl; add to the dry ingredients and mix into a soft dough
4. Roll dough out on a lightly floured surface, to about 1/2 inch thick
5. Cut into circles
6. Dust girdle with a little flour and cook bannocks
7. Turn them over when the bottom side begins to brown

Ale

15-20 lbs unmalted grain   herbs and spices of your choosing

1. Soak grain for in cool, hard water, draining and changing the water every 8 hours, for 30 hours. The grains should 'plump'
2. Strain grain (careful with all that weight or you'll get grain strain) and lay it out on mats for 5 days, stirring often to prevent rot. There will be odor. There should not be rot.
3. Dry in a warm oven if you are a medieval Scot. If not, a home brewing method is to put the grain into a cloth sack, tie it tightly, and run it through the clothes dryer on low heat
4. Now roast it in a large kiln. Lacking a large kiln, put the grain into your oven in parts: the first for 15 minutes at 225 degree F, the second for 30 minutes; the third for 30 minutes at 250 degrees F, and the fourth for 30 minutes at 300 degrees F.
5. Grind with a millstone. Lacking a millstone, use a hand operated grain mill
6. Steep the grain in hot water at 155 degrees F for one to two hours, using one quart of water for every pound of grain
7. Drain the liquid and rinse the grain
8. Boil for 1 to 1-1/2 hours
9. Add any herbs and spices you desire
10. Move to a wooden barrel. Let cool to 65 to 70 degrees F
11. If you are a medieval Scot, your barrel will have yeasts that cause fermentation. If you do not have a yeast-laden wooden barrel, add brewer's or bread yeast
12. Leave in a cool place with a relatively stable temperature, where the fermenting will begin
13. Skim off the barm that rises to the top, and save it for baking bread
14. Cover the barrel with a light cloth and leave for a day or two after fermentation stops
15. Drink and be merry!

Ale made this way doesn't last long. Drink it within a few days.

Amy Reads about Bannockburn

With chamomile tea steaming on the end table, and the last shadowy wisps of the nightmare warning her she wouldn't sleep yet, Amy threw kindling in the hearth and stirred it into a small, cheerful blaze. It would be mid-morning in the States—a perfect time to call her parents. She could tell Rose by breakfast that she'd done it.

Instead, she chose a book from the professor's shelf and settled into the arm chair. The wall lamp spilled warm light over *Tales of Bannockburn*, but her thoughts jumped from the pages before her to the photograph of Shawn upstairs, to Niall on the train, and back to the book. She made herself skim its pages. A parliament at Cambuskenneth. Raids on Northern England. The Declaration of Arbroath. She sighed, her mind straying back to the nightmare. She wished it would loosen its grip and let her sleep. But she knew the pattern. So, with eyes that refused to become drowsy, she read twenty pages on the days after battle, of Bruce's clemency toward Marmaduke, and his grief over the death of his cousin, the Earl of Gloucester, though the man had fought against him.

A tale is told, said chapter twenty, of a joust after the battle. Bruce held a tournament, pitting his Scots against captured English knights. Despite a severe injury at the recent battle, one young noble took part. He was knocked from his horse and, failing to rise, was carried from the field into his tent. Almost immediately, he emerged, blowing kisses to the ladies.

A smile tugged at the corner of Amy's mouth. It sounded like something Shawn would do. But he had died at Bannockburn.

Uses and Benefits of Chamomile

The health properties of chamomile have been known for centuries. Specifically, the German and English chamomile were the ones used. As an infusion (tea), tincture (in alcohol), or in creams and ointments for.

- Easing aching muscles
- Soothing cuts, scrapes, and abrasions
- Keeping skin healthy, improving skin regeneration
- Reducing swelling
- Helping puffy eyes
- Reducing eczema
- Calming upset stomach
- Promoting sleep
- Reducing menstrual cramps
- Treating irritation from chest colds
- Preventing gum disease

A note: Chamomile may be a problem for those allergic to pollen or ragweed, or using blood thinners. It is exactly for this reason that the above is not to be taken as medical advice.

Hildegard von Bingen on Chamomile

Hildegard von Bingen characterized spanish chamomile root as a 'healthy spice.' Other of her healthy spices include: water mint, mugwort, nettles, watercress, burning bush root, gentian root, fennel, psyllium, galangal root, raw garlic, spearmint, cubeb, lavender, lovage, fruit of the bay tree, saltbush, poppy, nutmeg, cumin, clove, parsley, polemize, wild thyme, tansy, sage, yarrow, licorice root, rue, hyssop, and cinnamon. She mentions several specific uses for chamomile.

- For vermin in the ear, cook chamomile in water. Let the vapor pass into the healthy ear. Block the healthy ear to keep the vapor in. Do this frequently.

- German chamomile is hot with a pleasant juice. It is a gentle ointment to painful intestines. Cook German chamomile with water and lard or oil. Add fine whole wheat to make a porridge. Eating this will heal the intestines.

- Menstruating women should eat this same porridge to "purgate mucus and internal fetid matter and start menses."

- For a stitch, mix the juice of German chamomile with cow butter. Rub it on the sore area.

NOTE AGAIN: this is a report of Hildegard's recommendations in the 1100s. This is not to be taken as medical advice.

Chamomile Tea

1. Pick chamomile flowers early in the morning. Do not get too much stem, no leaves, and do not use damaged or diseased flowers.
2. Pick and clean fresh mint leaves.
3. Put the flowers in cool water. Clean gently, removing insects and dirt. Soak them a few minutes after cleaning.
4. Strain with a colander and blot dry with paper towel.
5. Warm oven to 200 degrees
6. Lay flowers on a baking tray lined with wax paper
7. When oven is warm, turn it off
8. Set tray on lowest rack; leave door ajar
9. Check flowers occasionally. If not dry after a few hours, reheat oven and start again
10. Dried flowers can be stored in an airtight jar, in a cool, dry place, for six months

Tea:

1. Put 1 tbsp crushed or whole flowers into boiling water
2. Steep 10-15 minutes
3. Strain water through a sieve into teacups

Niall and Shawn Plot

Watching the sea of men flow across the drawbridge, Shawn didn't notice Brother Andrew at his side until Niall touched his sleeve. "We've business with MacDougall."

"They're leaving," Shawn objected. He didn't add that he had no desire to have any business with MacDougall.

Niall waved away his concern. "It takes a wee bit of time to get so many men moving. This won't take long." He pulled Shawn through the crowd, into the empty great hall. Checking that it was indeed empty, he put his mouth to Shawn's ear and whispered.

"MacDonald knows about this?" Shawn asked, dubiously.

Niall snorted. "Of course not. He's far too cautious. MacDougall will be here soon. 'Tis easy enough to get into his room. Just do as I've told you."

"We're dressed the same?" Shawn asked. Though he questioned the wisdom of the plan, he shared Niall's concern for Allene.

Niall looked him over and nodded, before disappearing up the stairs to the upper chambers. Shawn waited, beckoning a servant to bring food to one of the long tables running the length of the hall. He ate hot porridge, his boots scuffling the rush mats under his feet. His heart pounded; his insides turned watery. His initial unease with the plan grew, but it was too late. Niall would be in MacDougall's room. He finished his porridge and scratched the ears of a wolfhound nosing at his hand for food. His nerves stretched tauter with each second.

History

Since the late medieval period, oats have been a staple in Scotland. It's hardly a wonder, as they're a nutritious, sustaining food in a cold, damp climate. As with so many things, there are beliefs, or superstitions, attached. It was believed that porridge must be stirred only with the right hand, and clockwise, to ward off evil spirits.

In days gone by, the oats would be mixed and cooked with water to form a thick paste, cooled, and stored in a 'porridge drawer.' The porridge would be eaten from this over several days. When it became cold, it became even thicker, and could be cut into slices to be fried for breakfast or eaten at lunch.

Groats (the crushed grain of various cereals) boiled in water or milk made a thin porridge eaten in the Middle Ages. In more recent times, gruel has been food for invalids, often with lemon peel, nutmeg, wine, port or spirits.

Types of Oats Used for Porridge

In the world of music, every little thing matters—a new reed, the width of the rim of the mouthpiece, rose brass vs. yellow brass. Likewise in food. The humble porridge, in truth, can have many tastes and a variety of textures—thick, sweet, smooth, lighter or heavier. It depends on the type of oats used. Fine oats, for instance, will cook more quickly.

For porridge, the oats are usually rolled rather than crushed and the medium grain Scottish oats, also known as pinhead oats. These will give you a smooth texture for porridge, and are good for traditional oatcakes, biscuits, stuffing, or haggis.

Gruel

A typical medieval 'recipe' for gruel went something like this:

2 tbsp of groats or oatmeal   2 pints of boiling water
4 tbsp of cold water

1. Put oats and cold water, into a saucepan and mix until smooth
2. Stirring constantly, pour in one pint of boiling water
3. Stirring frequently, boil for 10 minutes

With quantities that small, I'm thinking this was a very poor and thin family who left us this recipe. For my family, we'd multiply all of that by 10. Or 20.

Porridge

4oz pinhead or rolled oats   Pinch of salt (optional)
9½ fl oz water or milk or a mixture of both

1. Porridge can be made with all milk, all water, or a mix of the two. All milk will give you the creamiest porridge.
2. Place the oats in a saucepan with milk and/or water.
3. Bring oats to a slow boil, stirring constantly, until porridge begins to thicken.
4. Lower the heat. Simmer for about 7 minutes, until porridge is thick and heated through
5. Remove from the heat and let stand for 1 minute
6. Serve with maple syrup, brown sugar, honey, jam, or lemon

Amy Talks to Rob

Amy slid a pan of fish fillets into the oven for dinner and returned to the living room, energized by Sinead's lesson, to play her own violin. As her bow danced through a Telemann sonata, the phone rang.

"Rob!" she said in surprise, when she recognized his voice. She tucked her violin into its case.

"Hey!" His voice came over the phone with what sounded like forced cheer. "How are you?"

"Good." She polished the face of the violin. "Great."

"You barely e-mail me."

She paused, startled at his presumption, then found her voice. "I've been busy. I started teaching a student. I just finished." She laid the cloth over the face of the violin and snapped the case shut.

"What else are you up to?"

"I go to the field." When he didn't answer, she imagined he must be thinking it was unhealthy. "I go to church," she added. "I'm thinking about going to Iona."

"Iona? The island? Why?"

"I hear it's peaceful." She hadn't told Rob about Shawn's message. She decided not to tell him about meeting the cop or heeding his suggestion to search for Niall's fate on the internet.

"Yeah." He was silent a moment, then added, "We miss you here."

"Rob, I'm not gone forever." She moved down the narrow hall to the kitchen, set the phone on the counter on speaker, and pulled a head of lettuce from the refrigerator, shredding it into a bowl as she talked. "It's a year, that's all."

"I'm just saying...."

"Tell me what's going on there." She didn't want to argue with him. She listened while he talked of the weather, and Dana, and the summer concert series. When he paused, she took a breath. "You're not telling me what they did about Shawn."

"I didn't want to upset you." He cleared his throat. "Dan found a guy on trumpet. He's got Shawn's charisma, but not his way of attracting trouble. He and I are working up some duets."

She checked the fish—it was a warm golden brown, and its aroma filled the kitchen—and listened awhile longer. Rob saw himself as the new best friend of the new star. She encouraged him, applauded him, and, sliding the pan from the oven, told him she had to go. "Don't worry about upsetting me," she assured him. "They have to move on."

Pan Fried Fish

PREHEAT OVEN: 400 degrees F

2 tbsp shortening or butter	1/4 tsp salt
1/2 C. finely chopped onion	1/4 tsp dried thyme leaves
1/2 C. finely diced green pepper	1/8 tsp black pepper
1 tbsp all-purpose flour	1 lb cod fillets
1 tsp brown sugar	1/2 tsp dried marjoram leaves

1. Grease a shallow 1 quart baking dish and add fish.
2. Saute onion and pepper in shortening over medium heat, until golden
3. Add flour, brown sugar, marjoram, salt, thyme, and pepper
4. Stir until smoot
5. Bring to a boil, stirring constantly, until sauce thickens
6. Pour sauce over fish
7. Bake 12 to 15 minutes, until fish flakes easily.

Shawn Wakes to Raiding with James Douglas

Shawn awoke bleary, rubbing dawn's cold mist from his eyes, squinting at the leather and mail-clad bodies rustling around him. He ran a hand through his hair, pushing it from his eyes. Some men still slept. Some sat up sleepily, while others moved, ghostly shapes through murky gloom, thrusting food over small fires or seeing to their horses in the gray pre-dawn.

Something was wrong. Shawn sat up, scratching his unshaven neck.

For a half second, he thought it was being in medieval Scotland's great Caledonian forest. He should be sliding from red silk sheets in his king size bed. He shook his head, squinting at pines, men, and ponies. He'd long since quit expecting to wake to the twenty-first century. He'd expected a medieval forest with fourteenth-century warriors. So what was wrong?

They weren't English, were they? He peered through the forest, to men stirring and moving, in tunics, and breeks of sturdy woven fiber. They were definitely Scots, with tartans everywhere. He threw the robe off himself. In any direction, as far as he could see, men moved through trees, pushing among gray tendrils of mist and silvery gray pine needles and birch trunks. He scrambled to his feet, straining to see, listening.

The man beside him stirred and stretched. "Cold day," he said.

"Aye." Shawn scanned the forest once more. "Where's MacDonald?"

"MacDonald?"

Mounting unease crawled up Shawn's skin. He gathered his tartan, tossing it over his shoulder, and pushed through the growing number of wakeful men, among the small fires. The first five didn't know MacDonald. The sixth, rising from his fire and gulping an oatcake, said, "Warn't he goin' back to Glenmirril?"

"Aye, he was," Shawn said. He'd walked far enough, pushing tree limbs aside and brushing against other men in the forest, to see there were more than a hundred men here. There seemed no end to them, in fact, forever appearing out of the mist and from around trees. Then he came face to face with Lachlan, the younger man from Glenmirril. They stared at each other.

"Niall!" Lachlan burst into a broad grin. He slapped Shawn on the arm. "My Lord Niall, you've come with us. I thought you were going home."

Shawn stared, unable to think of a single word to say in response.

"Did Douglas ask you to come along?" The grin did not leave the other man's face.

"Uh, yes. No." Shawn tried furiously to think like Niall. What would Niall do? *Maybe I can get myself a bracelet,* he thought with irritation. *WWND.*

History

At first glance, it is easy to think the Scottish raids into England cast the Scots in a bad light. The rest of the story, however, is that Edward I had spent years terrorizing the Scots, pressing his claim from 1292 until his death in 1307, to be 'overlord' of Scotland.

From 1307 to 1314, Bruce steadily regained all the castles Edward I had taken. When he defeated Edward II decisively at Bannockburn on June 24, 1314, this should have been the end of it. Edward II, however, steadfastly refused to acknowledge Scotland as the independent country it was. Without a treaty, without an agreement that Robert the Bruce was King of Scots, the Scots were still not safe in their own country.

The raids had a dual purpose. One was to raise funds to continue a war that would, by necessity, continue until Edward signed a treaty. The other was to pressure Edward into that treaty.

And so, Shawn ended up on these forays into Northumbria with James Douglas, who frequently led them. Why beef? Because one of the things they took, in particular, was cattle. The raids generally made a long U shape, heading south on the east side of England, and swinging back up north on the west side. While they also collected gold, or anything of value they found in the towns that didn't meet their demands for money, they ended up driving herds of cattle before them. It would have made sense to eat a few of those cattle rather than carry extra food.

There are no cookbooks left from the James Douglas School of Cooking, but we can surmise that building fires and cooking over them has not changed greatly. Were there spices in the forest? Probably not. In a larger army like Douglas's, there may have been some cooking pots, but in general, the Scots traveled very light, to get through their rugged hills and outrun the larger, more burdened, English armies. So we're going to assume that James Douglas followed suit.

Oatcakes and Bannocks

The first known oatcake 'recipe' comes to us from the 14th century French traveler, chronicler, and poet, Jean Froissart, who reported that the Scottish soldier carried a flat metal plate on his saddle and a pack of oatmeal on his back. `He casteth this plate into the fire, he moisteneth a little of his meal in water, and when the plate is heated, he layeth his paste thereon and maketh a little cake, which he eateth to comfort his stomach. Hence it is no marvel that the Scots should be able to make longer marches than other men.`` Is this a reference to the nutrition of oatmeal or the speed with which they were able to prepare their meals while marching?

In the centuries since, quite a few variations of oatcakes or bannocks have developed, along with beliefs and superstition. In some places, people poked a hole through the center of their bannock to keep trolls away. Some people sprinkled their bannocks with oatmeal before baking to prevent the fairies't taking them.

There were specials bannocks for the first day of each season—the bonnach Bride, or St. Bride's bannock for the first day of spring; the bonnach Bealtainn, the Beltane bannock for the first day of summer.; bonnach Luanastain (Lammas bannock) for the autumn equinox and bonnach Samhthaain (Hallowmass banncok) for the first day of winter.

There were more bannocks for other occasions. The Highlands had their bannoch Salainn for Halloween—a salty oatcake that was believed to bring on dreams foretelling the future. Yule bannocks, baked before dawn on Christmas morning, were also meant to help one see the future. This was a pretty easy method of prediction: good fortune to those whose oatcakes stayed in one piece all day, shattered dreams to those whose oatcakes broke.

Traditional Oatcakes in the Oven

PREHEAT OVEN: 350 degree F

3-1/2 C. rolled oats (not instant)	4 tbsp unsalted butter
1 tsp salt	1/2 C. water
2 tbsp flour	berries
3 tbsp honey	pine nuts, chopped

1. Mix oats, flour, salt, honey, then rub in butter until crumbly
2. Add just enough water to dampen
3. Divide mixture into two, pouring half into a second bowl
4. Add berries to one half and pine nuts to the other. Mix well
5. For dough into rounds, 1/4 thick or less
6. Place on greased baking sheet; bake 30 minutes, to light brown

I would think the Scots added what they liked to their oatcakes—whatever they found in the forest or along their path.

Obviously, however, they didn't carry ovens with them—especially not ones that could be pre-heated to 350 degrees! So here's a recipe for cooking bannocks over an open fire.

Bannocks over a Fire

PREHEAT FIRE: to hot coals, hot *glowing* coals if you're of an atmospheric mindset

	Bonus Modern Ingredients:
3 C. flour	
1 tsp of salt	2 tbsp of baking powder
1-1/4 C. water	1/4 C. melted butter

1. Mix ingredients, adding water slowly until dough is firm enough to wrap around a stick. If you are a medieval Scot riding with the Bruce (or anyone else, for that matter) you get only the first three ingredients. If you live in the 21st century, you may use the other two. Flour on your hands helps prevent batter sticking to your hands as you shape it around the stick.
2. Stick edges of dough together well!
3. Rotate slowly over the coals for 7-10 minutes. If you have a 'girdle' or a frying pan, the bannocks can also be cooked on these. Flip them to prevent burning on either side.

Dried Meat

While I have no research documenting it, it seems that the Scots would have taken advantage of the ability to dry meat, so they could eat on the move the next day. While not a medieval army, Lewis and Clark left detailed records of their journey, with some detail about how they ate.

Meat. Venison, rabbit.   (Salt and pepper)

1. Slice as thinly as possible, with the grain, into strips 1/2" wide and about 5" long. Partially freezing the meat makes this easier, but freezing is not terribly likely to be doable during the spring and summer months of campaigning in medieval Scotland.
2. Trim fat.
3. Cover the meat strips with salt, pepper. Leave out the cayenne because Christopher Columbus has not yet found it and brought it back.
4. Roast 5 to 10 inches above medium to medium-low coals for 2-1/2 to 3 hours, until the meat is dry, but slightly chewy. Add more coals as needed.

Rabbit Jerky

Here's a method that can be used at home or around a campfire.

1 C. salt for every gallon of water
In any combination: sage, marjoram, allspice, garlic, rosemary, celery seed, thyme, pepper, cayenne pepper, basil, cinnamon, tarragon, nutmeg, lemon juice, lime juice, Worcestershire sauce

1. Bone four large rabbits and, slicing with the grain, cut the meat into 1/2 inch by 3 inch strips.
2. Mix water and salt, and add spices as you please
3. Marinate meat overnight
4. Lay out on a cookie sheet and leave in a warm oven (maybe 200 degrees F) with the door ajar for 8 hours
5. Turn and dry for 4 more hours

NOTE: This will keep for several months in an airtight container. It will keep indefinitely in ziplock bags in the refrigerator or freezer.

Niall at Dundolam's Pub

Niall returned to the inn's dining area, a dark room with a roaring fire, heavy wooden bar, and a scattering of booths and tables. It was filling quickly with a crowd of working men. Three barmaids in white blouses, bodices, and long woolen skirts swished through the room, bearing tankards of ale.

A coin on the table brought him a steak pie, a pitcher of ale and talkative companions. Men did not call it wagging their tongues, but it had the same effect, especially as the Bruce's money allowed Niall to be generous with the ale.

He absorbed every bit of talk such as men might venture to spill: the laundress who trimmed men's hair and was free with more than her soap, the smith who'd had a brawl with a farmer, the lad and lass who'd sent up banns, Lord Duncan who foolishly thought his wife wouldn't notice his frequent trips to the kitchens or the comely scullery maid who worked there, the long absence of MacDougall at Stirling.

Niall stored it all away, telling them he was Fionn of Bergen, a traveling minstrel, set upon in the hills, and his instrument stolen.

Willie Brew'd a Peck o' Maut

> *We are na fou, we're nae that fou,*
> *But just a drappie in our e'e!*
> *The cook may craw, the day may daw,*
> *And ay we'll taste the barley-bree!*
> *O Willie brew'd a peck o' maut,*
> *And Rob and Allan cam to see;*
> *Three blyther hearts that lee-lang night*
> *Ye wad na found in Christendie.*
> *~ from Robert Burns*

Steak Pie

PREHEAT OVEN: 350 degrees F

1/2 tsp ground cardamon	1-1/2 lbs meat—rabbit, beef, pork,
1/2 to 1 C. broth	venison, in any combination
1 tsp cinnamon	1/2 tsp onions chopped
1 C. grated cheese	9 inch pie shell with lid
Dash of red wine	1/2 C. currants, raisins, or dried fruit
4 egg yolks	1/2 tsp nutmeg

The original of this recipe called for bell peppers. As these were unknown in medieval Scotland, I substituted onions. A steak pie, of course, would have had whatever vegetables the innkeeper decided to use that day. Turnips, tasty turnips, leeks, peas, beets, and more—but if you want a medieval dish, avoid potatoes and green beans.

1. Broil meat only to rare, and dice into small cubes
2. Mix with all other ingredients except of course, the shell (unless you really want to be a rebel) adding just enough broth to make it a little bit wetter than it was, and place it in the pie shell
3. Seal lid onto the pie; poke holes in the top to vent
4. Bake 45 to 60 minutes, till shell is golden brown

Spiced Mussel And Leek Broth (Cawdel of Muskels, 1390)

Shellfish were particularly loved during Lent, cooked in their own juices, with a little ale, or sometimes in a spicy pottage, like this one, with *powdour fort.*

MEDIEVAL:

1. Take and seeth muskels; pyke hem clene, and waisshe hem clene in wyne.
2. Take almaundes and bray hem.
3. Take somme of the muskels and grynde hem, and some hewe smale; drawe the muskels yground with the self broth.
4. Wryng the almondes with faire water.
5. Do alle thise togider; do therto verious verjuice and vynger.
6. Take whyte of lekes and perboile hem wel; sryng oute the water and hewe hem smale.
7. Cast oile therto, with oynouns perboiled and mynced smale; do therto powdour fort, safroun and salt a lytel.
8. Seeth it, not to stondying, and messe it forth.

MODERN:

Notice the recipe below simply lists some of the ingredients found in *powdour fort*—ginger, pepper, and cloves.

3 lbs mussels	1/8 tsp cloves
2 tbsp dry white wine	1/2 C. almonds, ground
4 tbsp double cream	2 tsp ginger, ground
1 small onion, finely chopped	dash of saffron
3 C. leeks, thinly sliced	1-1/2 C. fish stock
2 tbsp olive oil	salt and pepper
8 ouncesleeks, thinly sliced	1 tbsp white wine vinegar
2 tbsp olive oil	

1. Clean mussels thoroughly, scraping off barnacles
2. Remove beards. Throw away mussels that do not close when given a good tap
3. Put in a large pan with a dash of wine
4. Cover and cook on high for 4 to 5 minutes, shaking pan until mussels open
5. Strain out and reserve wine
6. In a separate pan, saute leeks and onions in oil until soft
7. Add remaining wine; reduce by half
8. Stir in ground almonds and spices
9. Mix reserved wine with fish stock
10. Add slowly to pan, stirring well
11. Simmer on low for 25 minutes
12. Strain soup through a sieve into a clean pan
13. Throw out half of each mussel shell
14. Reheat over low heat and stir in cream and mussels

Poached Fish

Sauce:

    7 sprigs fresh parsley
    5 sprigs fresh mint
    2 tbsp white wine vinegar
    2 oz. breadcrumbs
    1 pinch salt
    1 pinch ground pepper
    extra white wine vinegar

For poaching:

    2 fillets of salmon or trout
    1/2 C. white wine
    1 C. water

1. Heat wine and water in a pan, add fish and simmer 8 to 12 minutes, turning halfway through
2. Soak breadcrumbs in vinegar for ten minutes
3. Chop parsley and mint very finely
4. Grind garlic into the herbs
5. In a bowl, combine saturated breadcrumbs and herbs and garlic and blend smooth
6. Stir in extra white wine vinegar until the mix becomes more sauce-like
7. Pour sauce over poached fish

Pykes in Brasey

Pykes in brasey. Take pykes and vndo hem on þe wombes and waisshe hem clene, and lay hem on a roost irne. Þenne take gode wyne and powdour gynger & sugur, good wone, & salt, and boile it in an erthen panne; & messe forth þe pyke & lay the sewe onoward.
~ *14th century Forme of Cury*

In searching for modern recipes that use wine, ginger, and sugar, what I found was almost invariably Asian dishes. Hardly what we think of when we think of medieval cooking! Here are two.

Sauce Variation 1

1/4 C. red wine   2 tbsp sugar
2 tsp minced ginger   1/2 tsp salt

Sauce Variation 2

1/4 C. water   1/4 C. sugar
2 tbsp sweet wine   1-1/2 tsp minced garlic
1-1/2 tbsp brown sugar   1-1/2 tsp minced garlic

1. Put pikes on a grill
2. Mix together the other ingredients and bring to a boil; reduce to a simmer
3. Serve pikes with sauce

Amy Cooks Chicken with Mushrooms and Onions

Amy set the pan on the counter. She drew the back of her hand under her nose, blinking hard, before reaching for the chicken. "Yeah, I was angry at him for not being there. Although it's hardly his fault something impossible happened in that tower." Still, she'd spent the previous day angry, and the anger had brought the horse rearing back to life in her nightmares.

"He gave you reason to walk away, and if he'd listened, he'd be here," Rose said from the phone.

A chill touched Amy's spine as a thought occurred to her. "Or would we both have disappeared if I'd stayed there?" She slid the chicken into the pan, and washed her hands.

"I don't know," came the disembodied voice.

Amy shut off the water and tumbled fresh mushrooms and an onion onto a cutting board, slicing them wafer-thin the way Shawn liked them. "I don't hear you say that often."

"Hm." Rose sounded indignant. "I don't deal with time travel often. Of course, I've been doing some reading."

"That doesn't surprise me." Amy diced the onions swiftly.

"Don't be impertinent," Rose returned.

Amy laughed. "Yes, Miss Rose. What did you find out?" She sprinkled the vegetables over the chicken and slid it into the oven.

"Nothing," Rose said. "I've lived on the internet this week, in between rehearsals. I've searched every possible term related to Glenmirril, Iona, and Niall Campbell. And I'm still at a complete loss. What about you?"

"Like you, I've run every search I can think of. I've spent hours reading every book I can find." Amy sliced a green pepper. "Nothing." She rinsed and shredded the romaine. "Mostly, all the reading makes me think what it must have been like for Shawn, caught in a time like that. But I've about given up on figuring out what he meant by Iona." Her fingers worked quickly through the last of the lettuce. "It really doesn't matter anymore, does it?"

"If it's still eating at you, then it matters," Rose said. "You need answers. Why don't you check that e-mail now? Maybe he sent something."

Amy needed little encouragement. There was plenty of time while the chicken baked.

Hildegard of Bingen on Mushrooms

Hildegard regarded mushrooms as a bit harmful, though in degrees
—those growing on dry land and in dry air less so than those that
growing in damp air or damp ground, which stir up bad humors. Some
mushrooms, however, will not harm people, and even have some
medicinal value.

Her *Physica* lists a number of specific mushrooms, according to
which tree they grow on:

The almond tree:
The mushroom that grows on the almond tree is neither hot nor
cold. It has no value for eating, but if someone has worms, take a
mushroom freshly removed from the almond tree, hold it over boiling
water until it is warm and moist. Put it on the area where the worms are
developing to end the swelling.

If the worms have grown, dry the mushroom in a warm oven,
without coals. Make powder of it and place it over the area to kill the
worms.

The beech tree:
The beech tree mushroom is hot. It is suitable for those either sick
or healthy. Someone with a cold or a mucusy stomach should cook a
mushroom fresh from the beech tree with good herbs (we are not told
specifically what 'good herbs' are) and lard, and eat it after meals.

When a pregnant woman is exhausted with the weight of her child,
she should boil the beech tree mushroom until it is broken up, strain it
through cloth, and make broth of this juice and some lard. This should
be drunk once or twice a day after meals, to gradually lessen the pain.

The elder tree:
The elder tree mushroom is cold, and is good for neither eating nor
medicine.

The willow tree:
Hot and good to eat, this mushroom cures pains in the spleen, lungs,
and chest. Cook it in wine, with a little cumin and lard. Drink the broth
and eat the mushroom.

Heart pain often results from the lungs, spleen, and stomach's bad
humors, says Hildegard. The cure is a fresh willow tree mushroom dried

in the sun or a warm oven, ground and mixed with a bit of thorn apple and and a bit of milk from garden spurge. Drink this on an empty stomach.

For leucoma in the eye, dry the mushroom in the sun and save it. When needed, soak it in water for a short time, then shake out the water. With a feather, streak this water on the eyelids so that it touches the insides of the eyes. Do this three to five nights before bed.

The pear tree:
Cold and moist; little benefit, no harm. For a scabby head, squeeze the juice of a fresh pear tree mushroom into olive oil, and dab this oil on the head.

For mangy nails, take a pear tree mushroom as wide as his nail and dip it in ox bile. Place the saturated mushroom over the nail. When it has dried up, do it again.

The aspen tree:
Hot, slimy, not good to eat, and no medicinal value.

Oven Baked Chicken and Vegetables

PREHEAT OVEN: 350 degrees F

3 to 4 lbs boneless, skinless chicken breasts
3 potatoes, peeled and cut into large pieces
1 onion, coarsely chopped
6 oz. of mushrooms, thinly sliced

1 green pepper diced
2 stalks of celery, in 1" chunks
2 C. baby or regular carrots
1 C. chicken broth
salt and pepper to taste
paprika

1. Cut chicken and potatoes into large pieces
2. Grease a 9 x 13 baking dish with non-stick cooking spray
3. Put vegetables in pan; season with spices
4. Pour broth on top
5. Sprinkle with paprika
6. Cover tightly with foil
7. Bake 1-1/2 hours. Remove foil in the last three minutes

Amy and Angus at the Deli

Angus collected their food and coffee, and they chose a table just big enough for two. "Tell me about the States," he said. "I've always hoped to go."

"Which part? They're all different." She emptied a long, thin packet of sugar into her white ceramic mug.

"Where are you from?"

"New York, originally."

"Big place."

She stirred milk into her coffee. "You mean New York City? A lot of the state is farms and hills and small towns just like anywhere. Very beautiful, really."

"I hear lots of Scots settled there." He sipped his coffee black, watching her over the rim of the mug.

Amy frowned. "No, it was more the Dutch, really. New Amsterdam, you know."

"Are *you* of Scottish descent? I swear I see a bit of Scots in you."

She sipped her coffee. "Because of the black hair? That's Italian and a sixteenth Cherokee. The rest is German, Dutch, and a touch of Swede. No Scots at all."

He picked up his pastry, his head cocked to one side. "You're sure? I'm usually a good guess of these things."

She laughed. "Of course I'm sure."

He blushed. "Of course you are. That was foolish of me."

She studied her bridie, wondering how to eat it. Deciding Angus's method must be correct, and noting napkins aplenty in the holder, she picked it up. She could almost taste the pastry oils through her skin. Spices filled the meat, making her tongue tingle with the flavor. "I hope it's not a strike against me," she added.

Bridies

PREHEAT OVEN: 350 degrees F

12 oz. ground lamb	1/4 tsp salt, or to taste
1 onion, chopped	1/4 tsp black pepper, or to taste
2 tbsp beef broth	1 pastry for double-crust pie
1 tsp Worcestershire sauce	1 egg white, lightly beaten

1. Cook lamb over medium heat, until evenly brown; drain fat.
2. Remove from heat; stir in onion, broth and Worcestershire sauce.
3. Season with salt and pepper.
4. On a lightly floured surface, roll pastry out to 1/8 inch thick
5. Cut into 6 inch rounds and place 1/2 cup filling on half of each
6. Fold pastry over filling; crimp edges to seal
7. Brush with beaten egg white, and cut three slits in the top to vent
8. Bake on baking sheet, 30 to 35 minutes, until golden brown

Bridies 2

PREHEAT OVEN: 450 degrees F

1 lb lean minced beef	1 tsp dry mustard powder
2 rounded tbsp butter	1/4 C. beef stock
2 onions, chopped finely	salt and pepper to taste
	1 lb flaky pastry

1. Remove fat and gristle from meat; cut into half-inch pieces
2. Mix all ingredients together well
3. Prepare pastry; divide pastry and meat into six equal portions
4. Roll each pastry into a circle six inches across and 1/4 " thick
5. Put a little meat mixture in the center of each
6. Brush outer edge of half the pastry circle with water and fold over. Crimp edges together at top of each bridie.
7. Make small slits to vent
8. Set bridies on greased baking tray, not touching each other
9. Bake 15 minutes, reduce temperature to 350 F and cook another 45 to 55 minutes
10. They should be golden brown

Niall Plays at Christina's Party

Faolan tapped his toe, and they started a graceful piece, with the men and women executing mincing steps at a more stately tempo. Niall's eyes drifted back to Christina, considering. Her smile had not changed. MacDougall gripped her delicate hand in his like dungeon irons. When the dance called for him to hand her off to another man, his eyes followed, hard and warning. Niall drifted up a step in the melody. Christina's gaze stayed low on her companion's chest, until he handed her back to her husband.

As Niall drew in air, his thoughts drifted to Bessie. He knew only that she worked in the kitchens, a servant like his own new persona. But would a girl being wooed by the master of the castle, especially a jealous one, be foolish enough to speak even to another servant? Bessie was the safer path to try for information, but Christina was the surer.

The smell of cooking drifted up from the kitchens. Boys gathered at the far end of the hall, bearing great platters of food. Niall's stomach rumbled. It had been hours since the minstrels had been fed. He scanned the crowd again, and started, to find Christina's eyes on him, intensely blue across the room. She dropped her gaze at once. The bodhran sounded the end of the piece. Faolan turned to Niall. "Ye'd best hope," he warned, "that MacDougall does not notice his wife's eye on you."

Stuffed and Roasted Piglet

PREHEAT OVEN: 395 degrees F
14th century France

9 lbs boneless pork roast meat
2-1/2 lbs pork liver
24 chopped hard boiled egg yolks
2-1/2 lbs finely diced Brie cheese
3 C. peeled roasted ground chestnut
2 tbsp salt
2 tbsp black pepper

1 tbsp minced ginger
1 tbsp cloves
1 tbsp sugar
1 22-lb piglet
Marinade:
2 C. olive oil
2 C. red wine vinegar

Christina's feast will certainly have a stuffed piglet! In the kitchens below Creagsmalan's grand hall, here's what they would have been doing:

1. Chop pork roast and broil until cooked; cool, dice into very small pieces
2. Cook and dice the liver
3. Mix together pork roast, liver, egg yolks, cheese, chestnuts, salt, pepper, ginger, cloves, and sugar and stuff it all into the piglet. Sew closed with butcher's thread
4. Set piglet on a baking tray (in a modern kitchen, use kitchen paper on the tray), prop mouth open with a stick.
5. In a modern kitchen, cover the snout, tail, and ears with aluminum foil to prevent burning
6. Make the marinade by heating salt, olive oil, and vinegar until it just begins to simmer
7. Baste the pig with this marinade
8. Cook for 3 to 4 hours; baste every 15 minutes
9. Put an apple in the pig's mouth 15 minutes before taking it out of the oven

Sambocade (elderflower cheesecake)

Cheesecakes, amazingly, date all the way back to ancient Greece. One medieval version we have comes from the 14th century *Forme of Cury*

Sambocade. Take and make a crust in a trap & take cruddes and wryng out þe wheyze and drawe hem þurgh a straynour and put hit in þe crust. Do þerto sugar the þridde part, & somdel whyte of ayren, & shake þerin blomes of elren; & bake it vp with eurose, & messe it forth.

The medieval receipt calls for curds, sugar, egg whites, dried elderflowers, and rosewater. Most modern recipes for cheesecake—in fact all of those I've seen which is admittedly not a sample anywhere near as large as Edward's army—call for cream. Eggs, however, are a substitute for cream. Each 1/4 cup of cream can be replaced with two egg whites (*somdel whyte of ayren*). Here is one version..

PREHEAT OVEN: 375 degrees F

9-inch unbaked pie crust	1/2 lb farmers cheese
3 tbsp of dried elderflowers	1/2 lb ricotta cheese
4 tbsp heavy cream	2 tsp dry bread crumbs
1/2 C. of sugar	6 egg whites beaten until stiff

1. Soak elderflowers in cream for 10 minutes
2. Stir in sugar until dissolved
3. Push cheeses through a strainer with the back of a spoon, and mix with elderflowers and cream
4. Add bread crumbs and blend thoroughly (to stay truer to the medieval version, eliminate these and use a little more cheese)
5. Fold in stiff egg whites, then pour into pie crust
6. Bake about 50 minutes, until it's firm, but still moist
7. Turn off heat; leave cheesecake in oven with door open for 15 minutes

Sambocade 2

I include a second recipe because I find it interesting to note the differences and similarities between cheesecakes. We must remember, in reading the *Forme of Cury's* version that it, too, was just one recipe in all of the middle ages. Just as in modern times, there would have been many variations on any one meal.

In addition, we don't know, when we read of pushing the *cruddes...þurgh a straynour* what kind of cheese those curds were from. So maybe this is what the sambocade at Christina's party tasted like. This recipe calls for cloves and nutmeg. I list them as optional because they are not included in the *Forme of Cury*. However, they were popular spices in the middle ages, so it's reasonable to think some cook somewhere made cheesecake using them.

PREHEAT OVEN: 350 degrees F

1 pie crust	3-1/2 oz. butter, melted and cooled
2-1/2 C. ricotta	1/2 C. golden caster sugar
2-1/2 C. cottage cheese	1-2 tbsp rosewater
2 tbsp double cream	*Optional:*
(or 1 egg white)	1/4 tsp ground cloves
4 tbsp dried elderflowers	1/4 tsp ground nutmeg
3 eggs	

1. Mix together all ingredients except the rosewater and, of course, the pie crust
2. Add rosewater a drop or two at a time, tasting to make sure it's not too strong
3. Put filling in pie crust
4. Bake for 1 hour 15 minutes—until slightly brown and a little wobbly in the middle
5. Cool in pan, trim crust edges, refrigerate 2 hours or more
6. Leave out at room temperature at least 20 minutes before serving

Amy and Angus at the Edinburgh Pub

Angus took Amy to a small pub brimming with a lively lunch crowd of businessmen and tourists, and the rich, warm smells of meat, potatoes, and fish. "My treat," Angus insisted. "The fish pie is the best. Or maybe you'd like haggis?"

"I'd love haggis," Amy said. "I had it the first night the orchestra got here. Like meatloaf, only better."

"I'll not remind you what's in it." He laid down the menu.

She grinned. "I appreciate that. Now. What was so interesting?"

After he'd placed the order, he reached for her notebook. "First, let's see your notes. Sometimes when you read through again, connections jump out."

. . . .

"Seems our Niall's a bit of a mystery man." Angus leaned forward, his eyes alight with excitement.

Amy cocked her head, the steaming haggis forgotten. "It makes no sense. It says Niall Campbell from Glenmirril?"

"Aye, whoever wrote the records was quite clear on that."

Excitement grew in her. "I think this joust is mentioned in the books in my house! But not about the physician being called." She read it again, her finger running under as if to verify, then raised her eyes to Angus. "So first he gets knocked out cold and has to be carried off the field. According to the professor's book—if this is the same incident— he immediately sweeps out of his tent waving and blowing kisses to the ladies." *You are just like Shawn,* she'd said to him on the train. Maybe they were more alike than she'd realized.

"He's fine at dinner," Angus continued. "Chatting up lasses and playing his harp. Malcolm MacDonald—there's a song about him."

"There is?"

"Old MacDonald."

Amy groaned. "I thought we were being serious here."

"Aye, verra. Old Malcolm insists the physician must bleed Niall, though he's quite healthy at dinner. When the physician appears at the chambers, Niall himself answers, the picture of health, and says all is well and his services are not needed."

The smell of haggis drifted, tantalizing, to Amy's senses. She glanced down, thought of Niall praying before meals, and, even as she said an internal thanks, took a forkful.

Fish Pie

PREHEAT OVEN: 350 degrees F

1 lb haddock (white fish)
1-1/2 C. milk
1-1/2 lbs potatoes
1 oz. butter
5 tbsp flour
1 small onion

1 tbsp garlic
1 tbsp oregano
1/2 tsp ginger
1/2 C. grated cheddar cheese
salt and pepper

1. Bone and skin fish
2. Cook milk and fish together in a pan for 20 minutes
3. Chop onions finely and saute
4. Boil potatoes; mash with butter, salt, and pepper
5. Drain cooked fish, saving the liquid.
6. Flake the fish
7. In a separate pot, melt butter, add flour, stir in fish liquid, and whisk over low heat until thick
8. Add fish, parsley, garlic, oregano, and ginger
9. Put fish mixture in a pan; cover with a layer of mashed potatoes
10. Cover potatoes with grated cheese
11. Bake until golden brown

Address to a Haggis

Fair fa' your honest, sonsie face
Great chieftain o the puddin' race!
Aboon them a' ye tak your place
Painch, tripe, or thairm:
Weel are ye wordy of a grace
As lang's my arm.

The groaning trencher there ye fill
Your hurdies like a distant hill
Your pin wad help to mend a mill
In time o need
While thro your pores the dews distil
Like amber bead.

His knife see rustic Labour dight
An cut you up wi ready slight,
Trenching your gushing entrails bright
Like onie ditch;
And then, O what a glorious sight
Warm - reekin, rich!

Then, horn for horn, they stretch an strive:
Deil tak the hindmost, on they drive
Till a' their weel-swall'd kytes belyve
Are bent like drums;
The auld Guidman, maist like to rive
'Bethankit' hums.

Is there that owre his French ragout
Or olio that wad staw a sow
Or fricassee wad mak her spew
Wi perfect sconner
Looks down wi sneering, scornfu view
On sic a dinner?

Poor devil! see him owre his trash
As feckless as a wither'd rash
His spindle shank a guid whip-lash
His nieve a nit:
Thro bloody flood or field to dash,
O how unfit!

But mark the Rustic, haggis-fed
The trembling earth resounds his tread

Clap in his walie nieve a blade.
He'll make it whissle
An legs an arms, an heads will sned
Like taps o thrissle.
Ye Pow`rs, wha mak mankind your care
And dish them out their bill o fare
Auld Scotland wants nae skinking ware
That jaups in luggies:
But, If ye wish her gratefu prayer,
Gie her a Haggis!
~ Robert Burns

Sonsie	cheerful	*weel-swall'd kytes*	well-swollen bellies
Aboon	above	*sconner*	disgust
Painch	paunch	*feckless*	weak
thairm	guts	*rash*	rush
wordy	worthy	*nieve a nit*	fist a nut
hurdies	buttocks	*sned*	trim
pin	skewer	*taps o thrissle*	tops of thistle
dight	wipe	*skinking*	watery
slight	skill	*jaups*	splashes
Trenching	digging	*luggies*	wooden bowl with projecting handles
reekin	steaming		

History

The national dish of Scotland, composed of heart, liver and lungs of a sheep mixed with oatmeal, seasoned and boiled in bags made from the sheep's intestines, it is traditionally piped in at Burns Dinners in January, as *Address to a Haggis* is recited. The earliest records of haggis in Scotland go back to the late medieval period.

Haggis

Sheep's heart, lungs, and liver	1 C. beef stock
1 beef lung	1 tsp salt
3 C. finely chopped suet	1 tsp pepper
1 C. medium ground oatmeal	1 tsp nutmeg
2 onions, chopped finely	1 tsp mace

1. Trim excess fat and sinew from sheep's intestine
2. Place in a large pan, cover with water, and bring to a boil
3. Reduce heat; simmer for an hour or more until all is tender
4. Drain and cool
5. Toast oatmeal in the oven. Do not allow it to brown or burn
6. Finely chop meat; mix well with suet, oatmeal, onions, beef stock, salt, pepper, nutmeg, mace
7. Stuff this mixture into the beef bung till it is more than half full
8. Press out air; tie open ends tightly with string, leaving room for meat mix to expand
9. Place in a pot, covered with water, and bring to a boil
10. Reduce heat immediately, cover pot, and simmer for 3 hours. *Do not boil as this may burst skin. If it looks like it may burst, prick with a fork*
11. Pour a little whisky or Drambuie over your haggis

NOTE: The casing is not eaten in haggis.

U.S. Haggis

FDA regulations prevent traditional Scottish ingredients, so for American readers, here's a variation. It won't taste quite the same, but is still good!

1 beef bung (from a butcher)	1 tbsp allspice
1/2 lb old fashioned oats	2-1/2 tbsp salt
4 tbsp butter	1 tbsp pepper
1 large onion, chopped	1 tbsp mustard powder
3 lbs lamb meat, in chunks	1 lb lard (suet if available)
1 lb beef liver, in large chunks	1 C. beer

1. Rinse beef bung thoroughly, inside and out, then soak in lukewarm water for an hour or more.
2. Toast oats for 20 minutes at 350F, stirring occasionally.
3. Saute onion in butter until translucent. Allow to cool.
4. Mix spices, onion, lamb, liver, oats and lard in a large ziplock bag. Leave in freezer until very cold, but not yet frozen. It can be close enough to be stiff
5. Grind meat mixture in a grinder, or chop very, very small. Use less beer if you chop instead of grind
6. Put the meat in a blender on low for one minute. Add beer, and mix on medium for one minute, until everything is sticky.
7. Cut bung into three equal pieces. One will be closed at one end, open at the other, while the other two will be open at both ends. Sew one end of each two-ended piece shut with a butcher needle and thread
8. Stuff each bung bag with the meat mixture. Squeeze out air, but leave slack for the meat to expand. Sew each bag shut.
9. Bring a large pot of water to a simmer, and add the haggis. Simmer gently for three hours or more

NOTE: The casing is not eaten in haggis.

Miss Rose's Gingerbread

Amy leaned back against her seat. "My first memory of her apartment is the smell of cinnamon and apples. But what I remember most, is when she played at my parents' Christmas party. She saw me on the stairs, and smiled and kept playing, and every once in awhile, she'd smile again."

Angus chuckled. "Was that so unusual it stands out? Your parents never looked at you and smiled?"

"My mother says I was difficult."

"When you were *three?*" The smile fled Angus's face.

"I suppose I was." Amy shrugged. "They were busy."

"Too busy to smile at their daughter," Angus mused. The car slowed as a shaggy Highland cow ambled onto the road, swinging its big head to study Amy, its nose almost touching her window. Sun glinted off its bronze coat, as bright as Shawn's hair when the sun hit it.

"It's not like they're bad people," Amy objected. Although the window was closed, she drew back from the long horns.

"Of course not." Angus grinned. "Just busy. They're harmless. The cows, I mean. Though I'm sure your mum and dad are, too."

The cow wandered in front of the car, forcing Angus to stop. Amy's breathing constricted. She'd given a bad impression of her parents.

"What were they so busy with?" Angus asked.

"Meetings, business trips. How long do these cows block the road?"

"As long as they like. Your mum?"

"Shopping, nails, hair." She leaned forward, watching the cow amble another few feet up the road before tripping into the pasture on the other side.

"Verra important." Angus touched the gas, and the car moved again.

"She did a lot of charity work." Amy watched the shaggy red cow munching grass. It seemed mild enough. "She had to look respectable."

Angus shook his head with energy. "Oh, now, I'm not criticizing. I'm a wreck if I don't have my nails and hair just right."

"Stop it!" But laughed, her tension draining. "You are so criticizing. Really, she's a good person. She does a lot of charity work."

"A good person with great nails," Angus said. "And verra busy. No time to look at her child and smile."

"I shouldn't have said that." Amy gazed out the window.

"Why not, if it's the truth?"

"I didn't mean to make them look bad."

"Tell me about Miss Rose," Angus replied. "Cinnamon and apples."

Mrs Purdie's Aipple Tart

The bakin' at oor village show's the best ye've ivver seen.
Fowk come frae far an' near, frae ilka airt
But listen till I tell ye a' aboot ma guid aul' freen
An' the tale o' Mrs Purdie's aipple tert.

Pair Mrs Purdie took it as an unco fashious slight
That her pastry nivver seemed tae mak' the grade
For the judges didna even cut a slice tae hae a bite
O' the aipple tert that Mrs Purdie made.

It wis in an' oot the freezer wis Mrs Purdie's pie,
Sma' wunner that ma freen wis losin' hert
It nivver won a mention an' the judges passed it by
Whit could be wrang wi' Mrs Purdie's tert?

'I doot,' said Mrs Thomson, ' that the judges must hae kent
Her d'oyley' (upon which the tert wis laid)
For in ivvery flooer show roon aboot, the plate wis evident
Wi' the aipple tert that Mrs Purdie made

Last spring the frost had nipped the blossom: aipples there were nane
Dame Nature cam' tae Mrs Purdie's aid
For naebody had ony fruit, an' so it stood alane
The aipple tert that Mrs Purdie made.

Her aipple tert wis nae the best, nor wis it yet the worst
But by itssel' an' in a class apairt
Sae the judges had nae option an' they had tae pit it first
And gie the prize tae Mrs Purdie's tert.

She wis a happy wumman: she wis quite puffed up wi' pride
Ower the triumph that pit ithers in the shade
She'd be mentioned in the paper, tellin' fowk the coonty wide
O' the aipple tert that Mrs Purdie made.

The show wis ower: she picked it up and went tae tak' it hame
'We'll hae this tae oor Sunday tea,' she said
An' she proudly gethered up the winnin' ticket wi' her name
Aside the tert that Mrs Purdie made.

Bit then, pride aften gangs afore a fa', o' that I'm shair
She drapt the plate, an' crash! Awa' it gaed
It lay in near a hunner wee bit pieces on the flair
The aipple tert that Mrs Purdie made.

~ Anonymous

fra ilka airt	from every part	*aside*	beside
unco fashious	very vexacious	*gaed*	went
d'oyley	small round of lace		

Cinnamon Apples

PREHEAT OVEN: 350 degrees F

1 tsp butter	1 tsp ground nutmeg
2 tbsp brown sugar	6 large apples, peeled, cored, sliced
3 tsp vanilla sugar	3-1/2 tbsp water
3 tsp cinnamon	

1. Grease a large baking dish with butter
2. Mix brown sugar, vanilla sugar, cinnamon and nugmeg
3. Lay 1/3 of the apples on the baking dish and sprinkle with 1/3 of the sugar and cinnamon
4. Repeat twice
5. Bake for 30 minutes
6. Pour water over apples and bake another 15 minutes, until tender

Apple Strudel Muffins

PREHEAT OVEN: 400 degrees F

2 C. all-purpose flour	1/2 tsp salt
3 tsp baking powder	2 eggs
1-1/4 tsp ground cinnamon	1 C. sour cream
1/2 tsp baking soda	1/4 C. butter, melted
1 C. sugar	1-1/2 C. chopped peeled apples

1. Combine dry ingredients in one bowl
2. In another, beat eggs, sour cream, and butter
3. Stir egg mixture into dry ingredients just until moistened
4. Stir in apples
5. Fill paper-lined muffin cups two-thirds full
6. Combine sugar, flour, and cinnamon
7. Cut in butter until mixture becomes coarse crumbs, and sprinkle a teaspoonful over each muffin
8. Bake 18 to 20 minutes, until a toothpick comes out clean
9. Cool for 5 minutes before removing from muffin tray

With Miss Rose

A black dog raced up alongside them, barking. Rose reached down to scratch its ears. "Hi, there, Max. It's nice to see you."

"You know him?" Amy asked.

"I see him every morning. Say hello. He'll be your friend for life. Now what are you so scared of?"

Amy scratched the dog's ears. "They'll disown me." Shawn had threatened her with that fear, the first time she'd been pregnant.

"Hm." Rose climbed the stairs to Amy's bright blue door. "And if they do?"

"Well, they're my *parents,* Rose!" Amy slipped the key in the door and let them in the front hall, dim after the morning sun. Sadness suddenly overwhelmed her. In just minutes, the taxi would take Rose away, and leave her alone. It wouldn't take long to throw her things together and go with her.

"Exactly." Rose strode to the kitchen, where she lit the burner and started the kettle. "If they're real parents, they're not going to disown you over being pregnant. Not in today's world, certainly. I can't help but notice, Amy, that it's not your mother you told Conrad you wanted. So what if they really disown you? You have a good job."

"I have no job at all," Amy pointed out. "I take it we're having tea before you leave."

"Yes. Because tea and gingerbread make everything better."

Gingerbread

PREHEAT OVEN: 350 degrees F

1/2 C. white sugar	1-1/2 tsp baking soda
1/2 C. butter	1 tsp ground cinnamon
1 egg	1 tsp ground ginger
1 C. molasses	1/2 tsp ground cloves
2-1/2 C. all-purpose flour	1/2 tsp salt

1. Grease and flour a 9-inch square pan
2. Combine sugar and butter; beat in egg, mix in molasses
3. Sift together flour, baking soda, salt, cinnamon, ginger, cloves
4. Blend flour into sugar and butter, and stir in hot water
5. Pour into pan; bake 1 hour, until a knife draws out clean
6. Cool in pan for 10 minutes

Shawn Roasts Beef Over Fire

"We've pushed a good ways in." De Soules unrolled a map. The men, one of them shooting Shawn an ugly look, crowded over it. Firelight flickered over the parchment. De Soules stabbed at their location. "Appleby is two hundred miles from Stirling. We've done well, aye? We've a king's ransom already, cattle slowing us and a long way home. 'Tis time to turn back."

"I say push on." Edward Bruce's voice burst from the other side of the campfire, with the intensity and discretion of a charging bull. "We've got them cowering and on the run. Push on to London and force peace."

"A messenger came from Randolph today," James said. "He fears he can't safely guard our back much longer."

"Bah!" Edward spat. "A hundred Englishmen will run from two Scots. And he wants us to withdraw."

Shawn roasted his own beef over the fire, while the argument raged around him. The smell of burned fields and the pall of black smoke rising from the town hung over their evening meal. He was amazed it still affected him; he'd smelled it often enough these past days.

It seemed not to bother the other men at all. But then, this had been their lives, from earliest days. Among his 'men' were two boys who could not legally drink a beer or buy a pack of cigarettes in his own time. They should be playing in a marching band or shooting hoops or fishing with their fathers. Here, they terrified the English, burned, looted, and swilled ale.

"Home, then," James said.

Spit Roasting

There's not much to spit roasting, but for most of us, it's likely something we've never done before. If you ever find yourself with a medieval army on the march, or wanting to roast meat in the open for any other reason, here's how it's done.

1. Find two sturdy sticks that branch into Ys and a third stick
2. Dig a hole, at least 6 inches deep, on either side of the fire pit
3. Put sticks in holes "Y" side up and fill in well, building up a few rocks and some dirt around the base to help stabilize them.
4. Build a strong fire in the pit
5. Season meat as you wish. If you're on the march with James Douglas, this step will likely be skipped, due to lack of seasoning
6. Skewer meat on the long stick
7. Rest this skewer stick in the notches of the Y sticks
8. Rotate the stick now and again to cook the meat evenly.
9. Put a metal cup or pot under the meat to catch the drippings

Roasting over an Open Fire

Another option, if you have a frying pan or a grate, is this:

1. Find four rocks about the size of Hugh's fist with flat tops
2. Arrange them in a square, outside the campfire itself, leaving room in the middle for coals
3. Place hot coals from the fire in the middle of your rocks
4. Lots of coals=high heat; few coals=low heat
5. Set the pan on top of the rocks and start cooking.
6. Replace coals as needed to keep heat up

MEDIEVAL RECIPES: ON THE MARCH

History

Eating on the march is less documented than eating in the castle. We are left with many questions. What kind of bread did they eat—flat, unleavened, baked? Did they have meat, fruits, or vegetables? Did they carry food with them, eat from a supply train provided by the army, steal, forage, or hunt on the way? As with everything, the answers left to us will not apply to every era, every country, every king, or every army. But records occasionally give us glimpses.

Edward III—successor to Edward II, so very near our time—sent orders for feeding the army of Crecy that included flour, oats, cheese, peas, beans, salt pork, 213 carcasses of sheep, and 32 sides of beef. The flour suggests baked bread. Oats were likely used for porridge and oatcakes.

Records from Henry V tell of orders to Southampton's brewers and bakers to provide for his army, and we also know of a dispute between Henry and the castellan at Arques who refused to sell him food for his men—a threat of burning settled that disagreement in Henry's favor.

Sometimes soldiers bought their food from merchants who traveled with the army. Sometimes food was purchased in nearby towns—with threats of burning, if need be—and we know some soldiers simply took food.

However, this is the English army, which traveled notably differently from the typical Scots of the same time. The Scots were renowned for traveling great distances—up to 60 miles a day by some accounts. Compare this to Edward I, age 60, and his court traveling 19 miles a day in 1300 or a much younger Edward III, without a court slowing him down, making 55 miles a day in September 1316. These kings, however, were traveling on England's roads, while the Scots traveled in rugged hills.

The point of travel times is that the reason Scots were able to make such good time was partly their garrons—smaller pony-like animals, now extinct, which were fast and light, and well-suited to these hills— and partly because they carried their food with them individually.

One big question has been what leavening agents were used. Sourdough and barm are likely.

Flatbread

2 C. dark rye flour	1 tsp sea salt or rock salt
1/4 C. dried soup legumes	1/2 C. white vinegar
1/2 C. navy beans	2 tbsp honey
1/2 C. kidney beans	1 C. water

1. Grind legumes and beans together to make legume flour
2. Mix legume flour, rye flour, and sea salt
3. Combine vinegar, honey, and water
4. Make a well in the flour; add liquid and stir briskly in one direction
5. Knead dough on a floured surface
6. Divide into eight, flatten each, and pat into 1/4" thick rounds
7. Cook for two minutes apiece in a skillet

Oatcakes

2 C. rolled oats	4 egg whites

1. Blend oats and egg whites well
2. Spoon oat mixture into small cakes
3. Fry 4 to 5 minutes each side.

For a better taste, add a tsp of cinnamon to the oats and egg whites. I left this out as I'm assuming the Scots did not travel with cinnamon. In the modern kitchen, it's best to fry them in melted butter.

Niall Walked Through Walls, They Say

"The Lord o' the Castle, MacDougall hisself, he hated that man." He chuckled and spooned in a mouthful of meat pie. Sauce trickled down his beard. He grinned, licked it up with his tongue, and started the story.

"MacDougall, he was a guid man, he was. Treated my ancestors fair. But Campbell now, he was at Stirling with MacDougall. Threatening him, telling him watch his back. MacDougall, there he was, goin' to his own room, and Campbell appears outta the blue with his threats. 'I'm everywhere,' he says. 'Ye'll watch yer back every moment, aye?' And Campbell, away he walks down the hall.

"And MacDougall, he shrugs it off and opens his door and into his room he walks, and there's Campbell on his bed. 'Did I noo tell you, watch your step,' Campbell says, 'for ye'll never know where I am.' And he walks right through the wall, he does, and away."

A waitress appeared, setting fish and chips before each of them. Amy thanked her and turned to Angus. "How would he have gotten to the chapel?"

"What makes you think he was there at all?" He seated himself.

Amy hesitated, hating the evasions. It was impossible to tell the truth, but maybe she could put a rational spin on it.

"Amy?" His fork poised over his fish.

She bit her lip and made her decision. Rummaging in her purse, she found her notebook, and pulled out the rubbing of Shawn's symbol. She pushed it across the wooden table. "This was carved on the chapel wall."

Angus touched it. "That's what upset you?"

Again, she hesitated. She couldn't explain being upset. Shawn would have changed the subject. "I read about it. Niall used this as a mark." So much for honesty, she thought. Her thumb strayed under her palm to Bruce's ring.

"Where are you finding this information?" Angus's fork hovered over his forgotten meal.

She stabbed at her own golden fish, pushed it around her plate, and took a quick bite, searching for a story. "I, uh, I found it—well, I'd have to check my notes."

Meat Pie

PREHEAT OVEN: 375 degrees F

1 lb lean ground beef	2 tbsp cornstarch
1/2 lb venison, finely chopped	1/4 C. water
1 large onion, minced	1/2 C. grated sharp cheddar cheese
1/8 tsp beef bouillon granules	1 tsp Worcestershire sauce
1 bottle beer	salt and pepper
6 oz. mushrooms, sliced	1 pastry for 9" double crust pie

1. Put meat in a large pot and cover with beer, boil until meat is cooked through
2. Add water, onions, and bouillon. Cook until onions are soft.
3. Add Worcestershire sauce, mushrooms, salt and pepper
4. Combine 1/4 cup water with cornstarch, mix until smooth
5. Add cornstarch mix to beef; cook until thickened.
6. Cool to room temperature
7. Pour into pie plate, sprinkling the cheddar on top top
8. Cover with crust, crimp edges, and pierce top to vent.
9. Bake about 40 minutes, until the pie crust is a light brown

Fish and Chips

Peas:

10 oz. dried marrow fat peas   salt and pepper
malt vinegar (enough to moisten peas)   shredded bacon

1. Soak peas overnight, then drain
2. Put peas and bacon in a pot with water
3. Bring to a boil, reduce heat
4. Simmer until peas are tender, then drain well, saving liquid
5. Mash peas with unsalted butter, malt vinegar, and pepper
6. Thin with reserved liquid if desired

Chips: 4 to 5 potatoes

1. Peel and slice potatoes into chips.
2. Boil about 5 minutes.
3. Drain and set out on paper towel to get rid of remaining moisture

Batter:

self-rising flour   malt vinegar
water, beer, or ale   pinch of salt

1. Sieve flour and salt in bowl
2. Make well in center and add the beer (or water if you prefer)
3. Whisk batter smooth and creamy until it starts to bubbles
4. Add 2 tbsp vinegar

Fish: 4 haddock fillets

1. Heat oil in a deep fat fryer
2. Test temperature by dropping in a small bit of batter; if it turns golden crisp, the temperature is right
3. Dry haddock on paper towel, then coat completely with batter.
4. Place in fryer 5 – 10 minutes depending on size of fish; do not let it become too brown
5. Remove from fryer (or friar, if you have a problem with hungry monks in your kitchen), and drain on kitchen roll.
6. Keep warm in the oven, while you cook the rest
7. Cook the chips in the oil

Shawn's Meatloaf

Amy started dinner—one of Shawn's meatloaf recipes. It brought with it, as everything did, memories. He had made it after they had gone ice skating one snowy night, with the city lights shining on the rink outside the concert hall, and Christmas music playing.

He let her into his new house after skating, beaming. Moving boxes lined the walls of the two-story great room, beside a floor to ceiling fireplace with a pair of soaring windows on either side. "Sorry about the mess," he said. "I just got the keys two days ago. You like it?"

"Like it! It's incredible. And you're only twenty-two."

He threw his head back, laughing. "Amazing what you can buy with a couple CDs and a few appearances on talk shows. Want the grand tour?"

She hung back, hoping he wasn't going to be so predictable as to offer to show her the bedroom.

He turned left, past the great room. "You should see the kitchen!"

Surprised, she followed him. The kitchen opened up, acres of granite counters and slick silver appliances. "It's beautiful!" She ran a hand over the shining surfaces.

He threw the doors of the refrigerator open. "Deep freezer, extra wide shelves. Check out this oven!"

She stared in amazement as he grabbed a roll of ground beef from the refrigerator.

"What?" He stopped, staring at her.

"You," she said. "Excuse me for saying so, but you don't seem like the type to get excited over a kitchen."

"Because you never imagined I was the type who liked to cook." He was already tearing into the beef. "Open the cupboard. I picked up my secret spices. You can chop onions. The right kind of onion makes all the difference. And an egg, crushed cornflakes, barbecue sauce."

She stared in disbelief.

He grinned. "Don't believe everything you hear. Give me a chance. At least you'll get a really good meatloaf out of it."

She had laughed, then, and opened the cupboard, bare but for a dozen brand new bottles of spices. He had delivered on his promise of the best meatloaf she'd ever tasted, followed by a game of Monopoly and a ride home, keeping his hands to himself.

And now, cracking an egg into her own meatloaf in her own small house in Scotland, the pain hit her fresh: Shawn was dead.

Shawn's Meatloaf

PREHEAT OVEN: 350 degrees F

2 eggs
2/3 C. milk
1/2 C. well-crushed cornflakes
1/2 C. chopped onion
1/2 C. grated carrot
1 C. (4 oz.) shredded cheddar
   or part-skim mozzarella cheese
1 tbsp minced fresh parsley
1 tsp dried basil

1 tsp thyme or sage
1 tsp salt
1/4 tsp pepper
1-1/2 lbs lean ground beef
Topping:
1/2 C. barbecue sauce
1/2 C. packed brown sugar
1 tsp prepared mustard

1. Beat eggs, add milk and cornflakes; let stand until liquid is absorbed.
2. Stir in onion, carrot, cheese and seasonings.
3. Mix in ground beef
4. Shape into a 7-1/2 x 3-1/2 x 2-1/2 inch loaf in a shallow baking pan
5. Bake uncovered for 45 minutes
6. Combine topping ingredients and spoon over meat loaf
7. Bake 30 minutes longer, occasionally spooning more topping over loaf
8. Let stand 10 minutes before serving

In the Dovecot with Angus

"I've always loved this half." Angus hefted the backpack on his shoulder as they crossed the courtyard through grass still damp with the last rain. They ducked into the dovecot's dim interior. In close quarters, out of the wind, warmth enveloped them. Small openings high up let in shafts of sunbeams that cast down ethereal, hazy light.

"They kept doves here?" Amy wondered if Niall had come to this bailey. It had been the realm of the blacksmith, gardener, and tanner. The northern half had been home to the Laird and nobles. But he might have come here, sometimes. She touched the wall, seeking his presence.

"Pigeons, actually." Angus pulled a plaid blanket from his backpack and shook it out over the dirt floor. "Up to two thousand."

Amy pulled her gaze from the dusty light pouring through the high openings. "That's a lot of pigeon pie."

"You know about pigeon pie in the States?"

She helped straighten the blanket. "I had some last June. It was good." Niall had ordered it, in his brief time here.

Angus paused, a bundle of plastic knives and forks suspended above the blanket. Shawn's ghost hovered between them. He knew—at least he thought he knew—who she'd been with last June. Then he smiled. "I've not tried it, myself. But in medieval times, pigeons might be the only fresh meat they had all winter." He reached in the backpack, pulling out ham sandwiches, apples, and chocolate cake with a flourish that left her waiting for a white rabbit.

She knelt down on the blanket, glancing up at him. A touch of shyness crept over her. "How was your drink with Rose?"

"Fine."

Amy laughed, the shyness fluttering away as quickly as it had come. "No. Nothing with Miss Rose is fine. Loud, exciting, fun, interesting. But never just fine."

History

Pigeons in New York and many other cities are regarded as a nuisance—flying rats are among the disparaging terms used for them. In medieval Britain, they were the privilege of the wealthy and nobility. Dovecots—or doocots, in Scotland—round towers that could provide nesting space for hundreds, or even thousands of pigeons—were legally controlled. We have records of cases brought to court against those who built them unlawfully.

Arthur Cooke, pigeon and dovecot expert (yes, apparently there *is* such a thing as a pigeon and dovecot expert, and I'm not even going to make a bad joke about a pigeon and dovecot expert named Cooke while talking about dovecots built to keep pigeons to make meals!) estimated that by the 1650s there were 26,000 dovecots *just* in England!

To the modern city-dweller, this may sound insane. Who needs more pigeons? But it made a great deal of sense in medieval times. Pigeon dung was useful for fertilizer, gunpowder, and tanning hides, but much more importantly, they were a source of meat especially during the winter, when—due to lack of root vegetables—livestock could not be easily fed and kept over the winter.

Pigeons, by contrast, flew out to scavenge for food each day and returned to their sometimes very elaborate homes to roost at night. And when the feudal lord wanted meat—there it was.

Pigeon, when eaten, is usually called *squab*. Today, this means a pigeon, under 4 weeks old, although it used to refer to the meat of any pigeon or dove. Its meat is dark, like duck, but leaner, and full of protein, minerals, and vitamines. The texture has been called silky. It is also a rich meat, such that a small amount is sufficient, and it is best paired with sides.

Pigeon Pie

PREHEAT OVEN: 375 degrees F

5 pigeons, cleaned and dressed
fresh cloves
2 tbsp unsalted butter
2 leeks, white and light green
1 medium turnip, diced
1/2 C. sliced mushrooms
1/2 C. finely diced spring onion
1 C. chicken stock
4 tbsp heavy cream

1 tsp mace
salt and pepper
medieval pastry dough
beaten egg for glaze (optional)
into 2 rounds
Roux:
 1 C. clarified butter
 1-3/4 C. flour

Roux:
1. Melt butter over medium heat; whisk in flour for a rough paste.
2. Whisk continually as it bubbles over medium heat, becomes smooth and begins to thin: Roux will be white, blond, brown, or dark brown depending how long you cook it: 5 minutes, 20, 35, and 45 respectively. Stop at the stage of roux you wish to have
3. Pour onto a baking sheet and set in refrigerator
4. Cool until it hardened—several hours or even overnight
5. Store in refrigerator until needed

Pigeon Pie:
6. Put pigeons and clove in a pot, just covered with water
7. Simmer about 45 minutes, then drain, reserving broth
8. Cut meat from pigeon breasts into long strips
9. Slice whites and light greens of leeks thin, saute until soft
10. Add turnip, mushrooms, and onion and continue simmering
11. Add a little pigeon broth, cover, and simmer until turnips are soft
12. Melt roux and add chicken stock, cooking until thick and smooth
13. Whisk in cream, mace, salt, and pepper
14. Pour cooked vegetables and pigeon meat into roux, stirring well
15. Grease a pie tin and put in the pastry dough
16. Prick the bottom of the dough several times with a fork
17. Put filling in pie shell, then brush rim with beaten egg and water
18. Cover with a second pastry round, trim excess and seal edges
19. Poke vent holes pastry lid and brush with any remaining egg
20. Bake 30 minutes, until crust is golden brown

Chocolate Cake

PREHEAT OVEN: 350 degrees F

Cake:
2 C. all-purpose flour
2 C. sugar
3/4 C. unsweetened cocoa powder
2 tsp baking powder
1½ tsp baking soda
1 tsp salt
1 teaspooon espresso powder
1 C. milk
1/2 C. vegetable or canola oil

2 eggs
2 tsp vanilla extract
1 C. boiling water

Frosting:
3 sticks of butter, softened
1 C. unsweetened cocoa
5 C. confectioner's sugar
1/2 C. milk
2 tsp vanilla extract
1/2 tsp espresso powder

Frosting:
1.Add cocoa to a large mixer bowl and whisk away any lumps.
2. Blend butter and cocoa powder well
3.Add 1 cup of sugar then 1 tbsp of milk to butter and cocoa and mix on high speed for a minute.
4.Repeat until all sugar and milk have been added.
5.Add vanilla extract and espresso powder and combine well.
6.If frosting appears dry, add milk, a tbsp at a time until it is the right consistency. If it appears too wet and will not hold form, add confectioner's sugar, a tbsp at a time until it is good

Cake:
1. Spray two 9-inch cake pans with baking spray or butter; flour lightly
2. Mix well: flour, sugar, cocoa, baking powder, baking soda, salt and espresso powder
3. Add milk, vegetable oil, eggs, and vanilla; mix well on medium speed
4. Reduce speed, slowly add boiling water, and beat on high for 1 minute
5. Distribute cake batter evenly between the two cake pans.
6. Bake 30-35 minutes, until a knife inserted in the middle comes out clean
7. Remove from oven; cool for 10 minutes
8. Remove from the pan and cool completely.

Angus's Chicken and Potatoes in the Crockpot

"Dinner." Angus stepped aside, revealing a small kitchen. A round table, covered in a navy blue cotton cloth, frayed at the edges, held two place settings of beige stoneware plates, and dull, battered forks and knives. She bit her lip, holding back a smile. Shawn would have had fine linen, bone china, crystal, and silver, on his large mahogany table in his oversized dining room. He would have laughed this to scorn. She liked it. It felt genuine.

She breathed in the smell of roast chicken, lemon, and pepper. "I didn't know you cooked." She didn't volunteer that Shawn had loved to, also.

Angus beamed. "If a man's going to eat, he may as well enjoy his food." He glanced at the table. "I just threw an extra setting on, before I left, that's all. Just in case. Sometimes my sister stops by."

She smiled. "Does she?" Her stomach gave an odd little flutter. If Rose hadn't assured her, his behavior did. Angus really liked her. Trying to get information wouldn't leave him so flustered.

"Not that I don't want you here," he added hastily. "If she stops by, I'll not kick you out."

Amy laughed. He was as nervous as she was. Shawn would have a heyday watching the two of them. Nothing had ever made him nervous. But she had to tell him. Instead, putting off the moment she dreaded, she asked, "Do you want help with anything?"

He waved her off, already yanking the plug on the slow cooker and lifting the pot over to the trivet waiting on the table. He turned back, a quick step across the small room, and took a bowl of salad from the refrigerator. Seated, he bowed his head in quick prayer. When he finished, he heaped chicken and potatoes on her plate. They sent up curls of steam.

It was a lousy time to mention she was pregnant. She'd work it in during the meal, as they talked. She cleared her throat as she lifted her fork. seeing things."

… The doorbell rang, a sharp peal. He swiped at his mouth with a napkin as he rose. "I'm sorry," he mumbled. "Bad timing."

Lemon Chicken and Potatoes in the Crock Pot

5 lbs skinless boneless chicken
1 tbsp vegetable oil
1 lb baby Yukon Gold potatoes
2 medium onions
4 garlic cloves, minced
1/4 C. honey
2 tbsp fresh lemon juice

2 tbsp cornstarch
1 tbsp coarsely chopped fresh rosemary
rosemary sprigs for garnish
1 tsp salt
1/4 tsp freshly ground pepper

1. Rinse chicken and pat dry
2. Heat oil in a non-stick pan over moderately high heat, add chicken, and brown on all sides, about 8 minutes
3. Slice onions into thin slices
4. Put potatoes, onion, and garlic in a 4 to 6 quart crock pot; put chicken on top
5. Stir together: honey, lemon juice, cornstarch, rosemary, salt, and pepper, and pour over chicken
6. Cover and cook: 6 to 8 hours on low, or 3 to 4 hours on high

Rose's Seafood

"He's a good man." Rose lifted one eyebrow. "But very different from Shawn. No more backstage excitement." She set sugar on the table. "There's something special about that."

"No more working side by side," Amy added. "I miss that with Shawn." But then, she thought, no more questions and suspicions, gnawing like medieval rats at her insides. She lifted her eyes to Rose's. "No more surprise trips to Hawaii, no more lies."

"Is it a good enough trade-off for you?" Rose opened the oven door, pulling out a pan of scallops and crab.

Amy leaned against the counter, watching Rose. "It's beside the point. Shawn's dead." She sipped her tea before adding, "It's not as if I have to choose between them."

"What if you did?" Rose asked.

Amy closed her eyes, her hands wrapped around the cup. "Don't even say that. Something finally, really changed in him. We have a child together. How could I turn my back on that? If he was alive, if there'd been any chance of him coming back, I never would have let myself feel anything for anyone else. There was only room there because Shawn *is* dead, because it's over, no matter who he became in the end." She took milk from the refrigerator, adding, "It would be horrible to be put in that position. But he's dead. It's not an issue."

Rose piled the scallops and shrimp high in a serving bowl. "But there are other men in the circles you're used to—world travelers, composers, musicians. Will you be content with something so different from the life you had?"

Venetian Shrimp and Scallops

1 lb sea scallops
1 lb large shrimp
1 lb crab meat, 1/2" cubes
1/4 C. flour
salt and pepper
1 tbsp extra-virgin olive oil
2 tbsp butter
2 cloves of garlic chopped
1 lemon, zested

1 large shallot finely chopped
1/2 tsp crushed red pepper flakes
1 C. of dry wine
1 C. chicken broth or stock
14 oz. can diced tomatoes in juice
1/4 tsp saffron threads
12 leaves fresh basil, shredded or torn

1. Peel and devein shrimp
2. Coat scallops in flour seasoned with salt and pepper
3. Heat olive oil and butter in a large skillet over medium high heat.
4. When the butter is melted, add scallops, brown 2 minutes on each side then set aside
5. Add olive oil to the pan, then garlic, shallots, and crushed red pepper flakes
6. Reduce heat; saute garlic and shallots for 2 minutes, stirring constantly
7. Add wine; stir for one minute, scraping bits off bottom of pan
8. Add stock, tomatoes, and saffron threads; when it bubbles, add shrimp and cook for 2 minutes
9. Add crab meat and cook another minute
10. Return scallops to pan, cooking another 2 to 3 minutes
11. Transfer to a serving dish and garnish with basil and lemon zest

Allene's Wedding Feast

As a host of Douglas's men ushered MacDougall across the drawbridge, Shawn and Allene ran, laughing, across the courtyard to the great hall, decked with tapestries, ribbons floating from the beamed ceiling, hundreds of smoky candles scenting the air, and viols, lutes and recorders playing in the gallery. Allene's eyes lit with joy and gratitude when she looked at Shawn, and she danced and feasted with a liveliness all would take for a typical new bride, hugging him at intervals and thanking him again and again in hushed whispers.

When Niall's mother claimed her for a warm embrace, Shawn whisked one of the Morrison twins into a reel—at least he thought it was a reel—and spun back to Allene. While the Morrison twins and Lachlan's sisters surrounded her in a gaggle of giggles and blushes, he downed another ale, listening to Adam's grieving widow reminisce about her own wedding, holding both her hands between his. He did his best imitation of a strathspey with one of her seven daughters, while Hugh swung Allene to the bright melody of the recorder. Her face glowed. Candlelight and firelight glinted in her auburn curls.

Shawn danced something stately with Niall's mother. A veil held her tawny hair back, framing her patrician face. She studied him from under feathery eyebrows. "You seem—changed—tonight. In unusually high spirits."

He leaned close. "Next time you see me, remind me you like me best as I am tonight at my wedding." He grinned and winked. "Don't forget!"

"Niall." Allene appeared at his side, flushed with dancing, and glowing as only a bride could. "Your mother likes you best *as you always were*."

His mother smiled. "I'm rather enjoying his humor tonight."

"See," Shawn smirked. "She likes me best."

"Come away now, *Niall*." Allene's fingers tightened on his arm. "'Tis time for us to be going." They slipped toward the stone staircase, but an immediate flurry of calls and shouts dragged them, creeping, back. Allene's smile slipped a notch to courtesy. The blossoms in her hair seemed to droop.

Ronan claimed a dance from Allene, less thrilled with the festivities than she had been, while Shawn downed another ale, traded jokes with Lachlan, and did something circular and lively with another Morrison twin. "You look familiar," he said.... "Just how many Morrison twins are there? Have I danced with you yet?"

The Wedding Feast and King Herla

King Herla was perhaps the original time travel story, and known to those in medieval Scotland. As it involved not one, but two, wedding feasts, and Niall talks about the story with his friend Iohn early in the *Blue Bells* series, now seems a perfect time to tell the story. Get your popcorn (Recipe: go to a grocery store, buy a box, and pop it all in the microwave), sit back, and enjoy:

In a galaxy long ago and far away…well, make that *this* galaxy, in fact, this planet, but the long ago part is pretty accurate. In fact, it was so long ago, that it was long ago even to the people of long ago. It was that long ago that King Herla lived. Like all enduring myths and legends, there are variations on the story of King Herla, but the gist of it is this:

Herla was the king of the Britons more than a thousand years ago. One day, while hunting in an ancient forest with his men, he met a dwarf with a great red beard, and cloven hooves, riding a huge goat. "I am a king of many kings and chiefs," the dwarf told Herla and his men. "But I have heard of your fame and great deeds, even in my world. You are worthy to attend my wedding. We'll make a compact: even now, the ambassadors of France are arriving at your palace to arrange your marriage to their princess. I shall attend your wedding, and a year to the day later, you will attend mine."

It was as the dwarf king had said. Herla and his men arrived back at his palace to see the ambassadors awaiting him. The wedding was arranged, and in the midst of the celebrations and feasting, the dwarf king and his people arrived, great crowds of them. They brought food and drink in vessels of gold and crystal, in such abundance that King Herla's provisions went untouched. At cock-crow the next morning, he and his people disappeared back to their own world.

A year to the day later, the dwarf king appeared to remind Herla of their pact. A man of honor, Herla and his men selected gifts worthy of a fellow monarch and rode into the ancient forest. There, a cliff opened before them. They traveled into a dark tunnel, but soon enough, it opened up into a great cavern of light, seemingly lit by thousands of lamps. There, Herla and his men celebrated for three days with the dwarf king and his people.

Finally, on preparing to leave, the dwarf showered them with gifts of horses, dogs, and hawks. In particular, the dwarf lifted up a small hound to ride with Herla on his horse. "Do not get down from your horses until this dog jumps down," the dwarf warned. "Only then will it be safe for you to dismount."

Herla and his men rode back out of the dwarf's realm. Coming out into the forest, they found their world did not look as they'd left it three days before. There were fields where there had been forests, and villages where there had been only fields. Disturbed, they rode on, till they found an old shepherd. "Tell me news of my queen, wife of Herla," Herla demanded.

The old man looked at him strangely, and finally said, "I scarce understand you, for you are a Briton, and I am a Saxon." After some thought, he added, "I have heard such a name. But it is a very old story, of the wife of Herla. Her husband rode into the forest to celebrate the marriage of a dwarf king, and was never seen again. She died of a broken heart. But that was in the days of the Britons, and the Saxons have ruled England for two hundred years now."

One of Herla's men, upset, leapt from his saddle. He instantly turned to dust, and Herla understood that what the shepherd said was true. He ordered his men to stay on their horses. And so they were doomed to ride endlessly, and became the Wild Hunt, roaming the earth forever in their saddles without rest.

Until the first year of King Henry, in 1133, men reported sightings of the Wild Hunt. In that year, the sightings occurred in Wales, until shortly after, many Welsh reported seeing King Herla's men sinking into the River Wye. From then, they were never seen again.

The story of King Herla warns us against the trickery of the elder races, such as the dwarves, and the dangers their kingdoms hold even for the greatest among us.

In short, do not go to a dwarf king's wedding, no matter how much food and drink he brings to yours.

Potus Ypocras (Wine mulled with honey and spices)

Potus ypocras. Take a half lb. of canel tried; of gyngyuer tried, a half
lb.; of greynes, iii unce; of longe peper, iii unce; of clowis, ii unce; of
notemugges, ii unce & a half; of carewey, ii unce; of spikenard, a half
unce; of galyngale, ii unce; of sugir, ii lb. Si deficiat sugir, take a potel
of honey.
~ 14th century Goud Kokery

Most of the ingredients in this Hipocras are easy to come by—
cinnamon, ginger, cloves, nutmeg, sugar, and honey. Grains of paradise,
long pepper, galingale, and spikenard will take more work.

Spikenard, also known as nard, nardin, and muskroot, dates back to
ancient Egypt, and has been used in a number of countries and cultures
—Egypt, India, Europe; the Romans and Greeks. We hear of it in the
Talmud, Homer's *Iliad,* Pliny's *Natural History,* and Dante's *Inferno:*

> *He tastes, but tears of frankincense alone*
> *And odorous amomum: swaths of nard*
> *And myrrh his funeral shroud*

In the Bible, spikenard is used to anoint Jesus's feet, and the
bridegroom in *Song of Solomon* (*Song of Songs*) speaks of it:

> *You are a garden locked up, my sister, my bride;*
> *you are a spring enclosed, a sealed fountain.*
> *Your plants are an orchard of pomegranates*
> *With pleasant fruits,*
> *Fragrant henna with spikenard,*
> *spikenard and saffron,*
> *calamus and cinnamon,*

It is associated self-sacrifice, humility, and faith, and St. Joseph.

Throug history, spikenard has been used as a perfume, incense for
holy ceremonies, an herbal medicine (a member of the Valerian family, it
combats insomnia, among other things, and finally, in medieval Europe,
as a cooking spice.

Mulled Wine

After all this talk of spikenard however—which hopefully did not put you to sleep—I'm going to give a very easy recipe for mulled wine, with easy to find ingredients.

1 (750 ml) bottle of dry red wine	8 whole cloves
1 orange, sliced into rounds	2 cinnamon sticks
1/4 C. brandy (optional)	2 star anise
1/4 C. honey	

optional garnishes:
citrus slices (orange, lemon and/or lime)
extra cinnamon sticks, extra star anise

1. Combine all ingredients in a non-aluminum saucepan, and bring to a simmer over medium-high heat
2. Reduce heat to medium-low, and let the wine simmer for at least 15 minutes or up to 3 hours
3. Strain, and serve warm with desired garnishes.

Fake Hedgehogs

I have it on good authority that 'Kilt Thursday' is not 'a thing.' (I disagree—clearly it is, and you should wear a kilt to go to a Chinese restaurant every Thursday, because Kilt Thursday *is* a thing.) But regardless of my personal opinion, historical evidence proves that fake hedgehogs *most definitely without a doubt...were* a *thing.*

The medieval recipes left to us have multiple recipes for fake hedgehogs. We find them in the *Harleian* manuscripts, *The Forme of Cury,* the 15th century French *Viandier,* the late 14th century *Ménagier de Paris.* They were served during the funeral of Nicholas Bubwith, bishop of Bath and Wells, on December 4, 1424. Meister Hannsen, in his 1460 German cookbook, gives us three recipes for fake hedgehogs—q white hedgehog of almond paste (there are those almonds again!), a black one with ginger, spice, and sugar, and one of pureed figues.

Yrchouns: Hedgehog

Yrchouns
Take Piggis mawys, & skalde hem wel; take groundyn Porke, & knede it
with Spicerye, with pouder Gyngere, & Salt & Sugre; do it on þe mawe,
but fille it nowt to fulle; þen sewe hem with a fayre þrede, & putte hem
in a Spete as men don piggys; take blaunchid Almaundys, & kerf hem
long, smal, & scharpe, & frye hem in grece & sugre; take a litel prycke,
& prykke þe yrchons, An putte in þe holes þe Almaundys, every hole
half, & eche fro oþer; ley hem þen to þe fyre; when þey ben rostid, dore
hem sum wyth Whete Flowre, & mylke of Almaundys, sum grene, sum
blake with Blode, & lat hem nowt browne to moche, & s[erue] f[orth].
~ Harleian manuscripts

1. Scald a pig's stomach. Fill it with ground pork mixed with spices, ginger, salt, and sugar, but not too full, and sew it closed. Put it on a spit.
2. Cut blanched almonds long, thin, and sharp, and fry them in grease and sugar. Stick these in the 'hedgehog.' Put them near the fire and when they are roasted, glaze them with wheat flour and almond milk.

The manuscript that contains this recipe also has the menu lists for several feasts, such that we know *Yrchouns* were served at the funeral banquet for Nicholas Bubwith, bishop of Bath and Wells, on December 4 or 1424—second course—along with a number of fowl—pheasant, woodcock, partridge, curlew, rabbit, lark—and larger game and other side dishes!

So, we will give Allene a hedgehog for a subtlety.

Hedgehog

PREHEAT OVEN: 350 degrees F

1 caul	*For the spines*
1 lb ground pork	blanched almonds cut in sticks
4 lbs if using a pig stomach	1/4 C. suet or lard or butter
5 pinches of ginger	2 tbsp sugar
3 pinches of cinnamon	*For the glaze*
1 pinch of cloves	1/3 C. almond milk made from:
1 pinch of pepper	1/3 C. ground almonds
salt and sugar to taste	1 C. boiling water
egg	green and black food dye
bread crumbs	1/2 C. flour per 1/2 C. almond milk

A caul is a thin membrane. They come deep-frozen. Thaw it in cold salt water, changing the water occasionally. When it's thawed, spread it out. It holds the pork together long enough to cook into the shape of the hedgehog, and then melt away, adding its 'drippings' to flavor the meat.

1. Mix spices, salt, sugar and ground pork
2. Mix in egg and bread crumbs to help it hold its form
3. Shape hedgehog bodies, and wrap each in the caul
4. Cut blanched almonds into sticks
5. Melt fat and sugar in a pot, add almond sticks; stir until brown
6. Spread almond sticks on a plate, to prevent sticking together
7. Make almond milk: pouring boiling water over ground almonds, steep for twenty minutes, and strain
8. Roast stuffed caul for an one hour and a quarter
9. Remove and let hedgehog rest for fifteen minutes.
10. Divide almond milk/flour paste into two bowls, add green food dye to one, and black to the other. For black, use coloring paste instead of liquid dye. For the medieval method, use pureed parsley and pig's blood in place of green and black food dye.
11. Glaze the hedgehog black and green, however you like
12. Stick almond spines into the hedgehog's back,
13. Return to the oven, with the temperature lowered to 250°F for another ten minutes to set the glaze. Or just leave it to dry for a couple of hours.

Cockentrice: History

A fake hedgehog is hardly splendid enough for the wedding feast of the Laird's daughter, however!

The cockentrice—not to be confused with the cockatrice, the mythical serpent/dragon which could kill with a glance (must have been a mother!)—was a fantastical dish whose name came from *cock* (capon —a castrated rooster) and *grys* (a suckling pig).

Receipts for it are found both in the Harleian Manuscripts and in *Forme of Cury,* and we have records of it being served at a feast hosted by John Stafford, Bishop of Bath and Wells, on September 16, 1425.

Why create a non-existent animal on which to feast? No written explanation is left to us. Some guess that the creations harken back to classical mythology's hybrid and mythical creatures. Some guess they stemmed from the wild new creatures of the New World (which of course had not been discovered in Niall's time). But the answer I think is most accurate is simply this: Because we're human, we're bursting with creativity—because we *can.*

Cockentrice

PREHEAT OVEN: 375 degrees F

Stuffing:

2 loaves white bread	1 tbsp.+ 1 tsp. pepper
2 loaves brown bread	1 tbsp.+ 1 tsp. cloves
2 loaves grain bread	1 tbsp. ginger
4-1/2 dozen eggs, slightly beaten	few pinches saffron
3 c. sheep suet, diced	2-3/4 C. currants
3 lbs pork liver	4 C. pine nuts or slivered almonds
2 tbsp. salt	1/2 C. sugar

1. Leave bread out uncovered several days to harden
2. Boil liver until cooked; drain, chop finely or grind
3. Grate bread with a large cheese grater
4. Toss together bread, liver, and all other ingredients
5. Refrigerate the stuffing until ready to be used.

Cockentrice:

1 20 lb pig	1 large capon, 8-10 lbs

Glaze:

2-1/2 dozen egg yolks	few pinches saffron
2-1/2 tsp ginger	1-1/2 tbsp parsley juice

1. Cut pig and capon both in half at the waist
2. Parboil each for several minutes
3. Remove from water and let cool
4. Using a large needle and cook's thread, sew the front of the pig to the back of the capon
5. Sew the front of the capon to the back of the pig
6. Stuff both cockentrice and sew up
7. Roast about 3 hours
8. Beat together remaining ingredients to form a glazeb
9. Brush on hot cockentrice.
10. Return cockentrice to oven for 1 minute to set glaze
11. Brush with glaze and heat 3 or 4 times to reach a golden color
12. Remove from oven and serve your golden cockatrice!

For a very authentic touch, use silver and gold foil. It is edible!

Bread & Herbed Olive Oil Mushroom Pasties

Mushrooms of the night are the best. They are small with a red interior and have a capped top, and they are easy to peel. Then wash them in hot water and boil them. If you want to use them in a pasty, put them in with oil, cheese, and powder.

14th century, *Le Ménagier de Paris*

PREHEAT OVEN: 400 degrees F

1 lb mushrooms	1 tsp black pepper
1/2 lb grated cheese	1/4 tsp sage
1/2 tsp salt	1/4 tsp tarragon
2 tbsp olive oil	1/4 tsp garlic
1 egg	Pie crust

I am leaving the cheese unspecified as to type. It would have changed with the individual cook, the location, and the century. The cheese used in Glenmirril, in the Highlands would have been different from that used in France. So have fun, try different cheeses and see what you like!

1. Bring salted water to a boil
2. Clean mushrooms and drop them in boiling water for 30 seconds
3. Drain; chop mushrooms very fine
4. Mix in oil, cheese and seasonings, and marinate overnight in refrigerator
5. Cut 48 rounds from the pie crust
6. Line cupcake tins with 24 of them, pierce with fork
7. Fill 3/4 full and cover with remaining rounds
8. Beat an egg and brush it around the edges to seal
9. Pierce top once to vent
10. Bake 15-18 minutes or until golden brown

Mutton Saffron Soup

Yellow mutton. Cut up the toughest meat, which is the flank. Cook the pieces in water. Then grind in ginger and saffron, and add verjuice, wine, and vinegar.

14th century, *Le Ménagier de Paris*

2-1/4 lbs. leg of lamb
bone from lamb
6 C. water
1 C. sweet white wine

1/4 C. verjuice (or lemon juice)
2 tbsp. red wine vinegar
1/2 tsp saffron
2 tsp ginger

1. Boil leg of lamb over medium heat until the meat is very tender
2. Remove the bone
3. Stir in the remaining ingredients and simmer until the flavors are well blended.

Chicken with Fruit Sauce

Fruit juice for chicken. Take fresh black grapes and press them in a mortar and boil them into a broth, then strain them. And then from above sprinkle a powder of a little ginger and more cinnamon, or the cinnamon alone which is better, and then mix with a a small silver spoon, and sprinkle over bread or bread crumbs or eggs or chestnuts to bind it: serve it with red sugar.

(Note – Concerning this, know that orcanette is a spice that turns the color red and is also like galangal root; and is suitable to soak in wine and in water, and then crush.)

Note – if you want to make this for Saint John's Day and before one can find any grapes, it is suitable to use cherries, wild cherries, (guines), mulberry wine, with cinnamon, without ginger, boiled as above, with sugar added.

Note – And after if you can't find any grapes, as in November, the fruit juice can be made from sloe, without its stone, which is then crushed or broken in the mortar, to be boiled without its shell, then passed through a strainer, and with spices put in and made as above.

~ Le Managier de Paris, c. 1393

What I like about this original recipe is that it highlights how much cooking is an art, at least as much as the 'science' it seems to be, with its specific amounts of ingredients and step by step directions. In fact, cooking is like music: we can follow the score to get the same piece over and over, *or* we can improvise, fluidly (no pun intended, but hey, if the pun fits, wear it) making it up as we go along—although the ability to improvise is usually based on years of knowledge, experience, and experimentation in music. Maybe this is why Shawn is quite at home making things up in the kitchen. He *gets* music, and he likewise *gets* food—what steps will get what results, what foods go well together, and so on, such that, like this medieval recipe, he can freely substitute and shift things around and try new combinations.

Notice, too, that the beginning of the recipe sounds very much like making verjuice—crushing and straining grapes.

Since 'spice powder' is not specified, and since powder douce and powder fort were so often called that, I'm going to make a guess that we can use 'spice powder' for 'powder fine.'

To make your spice powder, from *Le Menagier de Paris*:

4 tbsp white ginger	1-1/2 tsp cloves
1 tbsp sugar	1-1/2 tsp grains of paradise
1 tbsp cinnamon	

1. Grind these together and mix well into a powder

Now, make your chicken sauce:

1 C. juice from equal amounts green and black grapes OR 1 C. of plumb juice	powder fine/ spice powder 1/4 tsp cinnamon 1 tbsp bread crumbs

Grapes:
1. If using grapes, put juice in a pan over low heat, add spices, and whisk in bread crumbs
2. Bring to a boil, allowing to thicken slightly
3. Taste and adjust seasoning if desired.

Plums:
1. Put crushed plums in pan; cook until tender and most of the juice has been extracted
2. Strain and retain juice
3. Add bread crumbs and spices and heat to boiling, allow to thicken.

Venison Pie

To bake Veneson. Take nothynge but pepper and salte, but lette it haue
ynoughe, and yf the Veneson be leane, larde it throughe wyth bacon.
~ *England, 15ᵗʰ Century, A Proper Newe Booke of Cokerye*

To bake Veneson. Take nothynge but pepper and salte, but lette it haue
ynoughe, and yf the Veneson be leane, larde it throughe wyth bacon.
~ *Harleian manuscripts*

PREHEAT OVEN: 350 degrees F

2 lbs ground venison
1/2 lb chopped bacon
1/2 tsp pepper
salt to taste

1 tsp ginger
1/2 tsp grains of paradise
pie crust

1. Mix venison, bacon, and spices and put it in the pie crust
2. Bake 45-50 minutes

Candied Orange Peel

Candied Orange Slices – To make candied orange peel, take five pieces of orange peel and scrape with a knife the white inside. Then put them to soak in good, clean water for nine days, changing the water each day. Then boil them in clean water once, and then lay them out on fabric and let them dry well. Then put them in a pot with honey and cover it and let it cook over a small fire, and when you think that the honey is cooked (to see if the honey is cooked, put some water in a bowl, and put a drop of honey in the water and if it spreads it isn't yet cooked and if you put a drop of honey in the water and it doesn't spread, it is cooked) you must take the orange peels and lay them out, and sprinkle ginger above it, then more, and so on. And leave a month or more, then eat.
~ Le Managier de Paris, c 1393

Candied orange peel is one of the simplest recipes, and something I used to make with my children, completely unaware that it dated back to medieval days.

peels off 6 oranges	granulated ginger
2 C. sugar	1/4 C. honey

1. Bring orange peels to a boil in 6 cups water
2. Simmer 30 minutes, drain, boil a second time with fresh water
3. Gently scrape off any white membrane still on peels
4. Cut peels into narrow strips
5. Combine sugar, honey, and 1 cup hot water
6. Stir over low heat until honey dissolves
7. Add orange peel; simmer 8 to 9 minutes until peels are translucent
8. Drain water
9. Roll peels in granulated sugar and ginger.

Pears in Honey

Around All Saint's Day, take large turnips and peel them and cut them into four sections, and then put them in water to cook. And when they have cooked a little, take them out and put them in cold water to soften, and then let them dry. Then take the honey and melt it as you did with the nuts, and watch that you do not cook the turnips too much.
Note: On All Saint's Day, take as many carrots as you will want, and when they are well-peeled and sliced into pieces, they will be cooked like the turnips. (Carrots are red roots that are sold at the market by the handful, and each handful costs one silver.)
Note: Take choke pears and cut them into four pieces, and cook them as you did the turnips, but do not peel them. And do to them the same as you did to the pears.

~ *Le Managier de Paris, c 1393*

pears, quartered, core removed   honey

1. Parboil pears just a minute or two, then put in cold water to stop them cooking
2. Heat honey to almost boiling, not quite, and remove the white scum that rises
3. Skim until very little more appears
4. Let honey cool until you can touch it
5. Dip pears and serve

Shawn Serves the Venison

Niall liked Jesus, did he? Shawn marched through dim, torch-lit halls to the kitchen, where he demanded to carry up the venison. "They said he was a good man," he heard Bessie whisper as he passed.

Good man, bah! He stormed up the stairs, past smoky torches, bearing the platter high over his head. The real Niall was upstairs, too arrogant to lift a finger for himself!

Niall's mother, sister, nephew, and MacDonald himself, gaped when Shawn marched into the great hall, and dropped the silver tray heaped with venison with a loud report on the head table.

"Let the servants rest!" he shouted, turning and piercing Hugh, Darnley, and Morrison, one after another, with furious eyes.

Conal half-rose from his seat beside Morrison. "Niall...."

"Look at all of you sitting around!" Shawn planted his hands on the table, going nose to nose with the young lord. "Demanding to be served! Didn't Jesus say the greatest must serve? Didn't Jesus wash the disciples' underwear or something?"

Conal dropped into his seat. Ladies gasped. Allene's hand flew to her mouth. She looked to her father in horror. The Laird slowly gathered his jaw up, meeting Shawn's eyes. He planted his hands on the table, rising. Shawn glared back, challenging him.

Then suddenly, MacDonald smiled, threw back his head with a giant guffaw, and shouted, "Yes, do as Niall says. Let the servants sit!"

Roe Deer

France, 14th Century, *Enseignements qui enseingnent a apareillier toutes manieres de viandes*

2 lbs venison steak	1/2 tsp ginger
2 C. almond milk	salt to taste
2 cloves garlic, minced	lard or butter
1/2 tsp cinnamon	

1. Roast unseasoned venison until just done, adding butter or lard
2. While it cools, mix remaining ingredients in a pot
3. Bring to a low boil, then simmer until thick
4. Cut venison into thin strips.
5. Sautée in lard or butter until heated; top with sauce and serve

Book Three: THE WATER IS WIDE

History

Amy now knows that Shawn is alive. Shawn, meanwhile, is living in 1315 and the first half of 1316—years during which the Bruce and Scotland continued to press for Edward II to sign a peace treaty.

These were years of Douglas's raids into northern England, continuing to raise men—which, Shawn finds out sometimes means boys—to fight for Scotland, and Niall and Shawn spending a great deal more time together as they work side by side for the Bruce.

1315 was also the beginning of heavy rains and livestock disease throughout Europe, which led to famine, even as armies burned what crops did survive.

Throughout, Shawn and Niall seek a way to get Shawn home, while Angus—finally seeing the truth of what happened to Amy's 'missing' boyfriend, knows he must help get Shawn back, regardless of the cost to himself.

Steak Pie with Angus at the Pub

The waitress backs through the kitchen door, a tray high over her head. At the hearth, the dog thumps his tail. She slides steaming plates in front of us.

Thanking her, Angus takes a mouthful of steak pie, his expression confirming that regardless of never having heard anything about it, it is, in fact, delicious. He sits back. "Tell me everything. From the start."

I tell him, from leaving Shawn in the tower to the apology carved on Hugh's rock. The stress of the last months melts with each word. No more lying, no more evading. And he hasn't left! He's here, talking to me as if I'm not crazy! "I thought he was dead," I finish. "I saw him cut nearly in half. I thought Niall left the mark in Creagsmalan's chapel before he got thrown in the dungeon."

Steak Pie

Puff Pastry:

5 C. bread flour	2 C. water, or as needed
2-1/2 tsp salt	2 C. unsalted butter

1. Mix flour and salt; slowly stir in water until dough holds together
2. Shape dough into a flat ball; let rest for 10 minutes
3. Press butter between pieces of plastic wrap to make a 'button'
4. Refrigerate until firm, usually about 20 minutes
5. Roll dough on a lightly floured board, to a 1/2 inch thick rectangle
6. Put chilled butter in the center
7. Fold ends of dough over the butter, enclosing it
8. Roll dough *without letting butter break through,* to 1/2 inch thick
9. Rotate 90 degrees and roll into a rectangle again
10. Fold into thirds—the first 'turn.'
11. Put dough on baking sheet and make two pokes in it with your finger—the second 'turn.'
12. Wrap in plastic wrap and refrigerate 30 minutes or more
13. Repeat rolling, folding, and turning two more times
14. Refrigerate until firm; repeat two more times for six 'turns'
15. Wrap and refrigerate to use for later OR
16. Roll it out to 1/4" or thicker and use with a recipe

Meat Filling

PREHEAT OVEN: 400 degrees F

1 tbsp vegetable oil	1 oz. dry mushroom gravy mix
1 lb beef stew meat	1 C. water
1 large onion, chopped	

1. Brown meat in oil over medium-high heat and dice into cubes
2. Add onion, cook until tender, about 5 minutes, stirring
3. Stir in gravy mix, water, Worcestershire sauce, salt, and pepper
4. Turn heat to low; simmer 25 minutes, and move to casserole dish
5. Cover dish with puff pastry, seal edges to rim
6. With a fork, whisk together egg and 1 tbsp of water
7. Brush top of the pastry
8. Bake 20 minutes until the pastry is puffed and golden brown

Shawn and Niall Await the Fairy Queen

Dawn rose on the third day, pink rays streaming over the eastern mountains, lighting the night's mist into a magical morning landscape. Shawn sat against a tree halfway up the slope, staring down the mountainside. He hadn't expected anything, he told himself. Through days of climbing the hill, traipsing through the valley, exploring the old Roman fort at the top, and searching for anything unusual, for anything to explain Thomas the Rhymer's disappearance, he hadn't expected anything. The story was too ridiculous.

And yet—he'd hoped. Images of Amy had burned before his eyes and in his heart, as he climbed each slope, and searched rocks, and followed streams, as he hunted with Niall and gathered berries and fixed more oatcakes. Thoughts of her home in the States with Rob had plagued him. That he'd never see his child, never even know if he had a son or daughter, haunted him. That they were heading into enemy territory to spy terrified him. If they both ended up in a dungeon, there was no one to rescue them this time.

History

Thomas the Rhymer—and the fairy queen whom Shawn and Niall seek—is a fascinating story. Thomas was the laird of Erceldoune, also known as Thomas Learmonth, and True Thomas, adviser to Alexander III, a poet and prophet, who died in 1298, the year Niall would have turned two.

The story is that Thomas disappeared for seven years, returning with the claim that he had gone with the Queen of Elfland for only three days. On his return, he was said to have the gift of prophecy, and to be unable to tell a lie.

On their way to do business for the Bruce, Niall and Shawn stop in the Eildon Hills (pronounced EYE-dun) where Thomas had lived only 17 years previously, hoping against hope to meet this fairy queen in whom neither believes, as she seems to have some control over time and might be able to get Shawn home.

Oatcakes

In truth, Niall and Shawn would have simply mixed their oats with water and fried them. So for the authentic experience, leave out most of these ingredients.

2 C. rolled oats

1 tsp cinnamon (optional)

4 egg whites (optional)

butter for frying (optional)

1. Mix oats, cinnamon, and egg whites
2. Heat butter in a pan over medium heat.
3. Form oat mixture into small cakes; fry 4 to 5 minutes per side

Meeting Red

He hit a wrong note, and tried again, playing the phrase over and over until he was sure it would come out right in Carlisle.

"What a bollox." Grinning, Niall appeared at the doorway, a skinned squirrel skewered on a stick. He held it over the flames, even as he added more twigs.

"Yeah, well." Shawn grinned back. "At least I never tried to serve roadkill for breakfast at a five-star Roamin' Inn." He switched from their medieval Gaelic to modern English, trusting Niall had retained plenty. It was one language they could be absolutely sure Red wouldn't understand. "We better decide quick before he wakes up who's Brother Andrew and who's Milord Niall as long as he's with us."

"You've the hair," Niall said.

"And it never looked better," Shawn cracked. He peeled off the robe he wore, and tossed it to Niall. "What do we do with him?" he asked, as Niall pulled it on. "We can't leave him, and we can't take him with us." Shawn studied the boy. He guessed him to be about fourteen. They'd tackled and pulled knives on a fourteen-year-old. Was that about how old Clarence had been when he first met him? About. He'd been a kid himself. He'd never thought about where Clarence was when he didn't live with them.

"As long as the pony is lame, we're not going anywhere," Niall replied.

"He said he could help it. Do you think he was just talking to try to save himself?"

Rotating the squirrel over the flames, Niall shrugged. "Time will tell."

Shawn turned back to the lute, working on another piece, sounding out chords, while the smell of roasting meat gradually filled the small cell, and pink sunlight glowed through the door. The boy stirred. Niall pulled his hood up, and lowered his head over the squirrel.

Red opened his eyes first in a daze, looking confused, then suddenly scrambled up, scooting across the floor, till he bumped up against the stone wall, staring at Shawn with wide eyes. "Don't kill me, Milord!"

"I'm not going to kill you." Switching back to medieval Gaelic, Shawn put the lute down. "Listen...Red. You want me to call you Red?"

The boy shrugged. "As you please, Milord."

"No, really, as you please," Shawn said. "It's your name, after all."

"Milord, I've been called nothing else."

"Frank, Benjamin, Joe, Gene Krupa, Glenn, Benny, Amadeus. You could pick anything."

From under the hood came a grunt, and Niall spoke in their modern English. "'Tis naught but a name. We've bigger things to worry about."

"A name is important," Shawn argued, using the same tongue.

"Not as important as getting information. Which means healing this hobin."

The boy looked back and forth between them. "Milord," he asked softly. "What manner of monk is this? What language does he speak?"

"Brother Andrew," Shawn said. "He's a manner of monk who is completely unable to keep his vow of silence. I hope you'll pray for him."

"Find out what he can do," Niall said irritably.

"Red it is, then," Shawn addressed the boy. "Unless you change your mind. The world's your oyster, Kid."

"Milord?"

"Ask him," Niall hissed from under the hood. Red glanced at him fearfully; his eyes traveled to the squirrel, now roasted dark.

"You said last night you can help our pony," Shawn said.

Red's eyes lingered on the meat.

"Give him something to eat," Shawn said.

Red shook his head quickly. "Oh, no, Milord. Only if there are scraps."

Shawn rolled his eyes. "'Tis my royal command. Eat."

The boy paused only long enough to attempt to look courteous, before his hand flashed out to the skewer Niall offered, nearly burning himself as he dug in.

Shawn watched, wondering how long ago the soldiers had killed the farrier, and how long it had been since the child had eaten. He ripped with his teeth, gulped, wiped at his chin, digging around the bones with his fingers for the smallest pieces of flesh still clinging there.

When he finished, he looked up, suddenly abashed. Sunlight cast rosy shades over the stone walls behind his head. "My apologies, Milord. 'Tis sorry I am. I was hungry. I forgot myself."

~

Let food be thy medicine, and let thy medicine be food.
~Hippocrates

The Roman Fort

As with everything in my books, the locations and histories are as accurate as I can make them. The Roman fort where Niall and Shawn meet Red was known to the Romans as Cilurnum. It is known to us today as Chester's Roman Fort.

Built about 124 A.D., it was used, housing 500 soldiers, until the Roman's left Britain in the 5th century. It was nearly 1200 years old when Shawn and Niall were there 700 years ago! Today, you can tour it and see mostly the remaining outlines of the foundations—but you can see the actual house, or cellar, mostly underground, where Niall and Shawn built their fire and spent the night.

Squirrel ala Roman Fort

Like oatcakes, there's not much of a 'recipe' for squirrel in the wild, as there aren't many ingredients available. There are a few things that help, though.

1. Make a spit with a green branch.
2. Find a stick with branches coming off of it about the middle of its length. Trim these down short, and use them to skewer the squirrel more firmly onto the stick.
3. Put the squirrel on the spit. Roast until golden brown. The meat will be nearly falling off the bones.

For those who have access to a little more, or for days when Shawn and Niall may have eaten in a place with more ingredients, try this:

Squirrel de Paris

Le Menagier de Paris gives his young bride a 'recipe' that leaves much to the imagination. It simply advises that squirrels be singed, gutted, trussed, roasted, and eaten with cameline sauce, or put in a pastry with wild duck sauce. **(see p. 272)**

Cameline Sauce

Luckily, the 14th Century *Le Viandier de Taillevent* tells us that cameline sauce involves 'a great deal of cinnamon,' cloves, grains of paradise, mace, and bread moistened in vinegar.

1 C. cider vinegar	1/4 tsp cloves
1 C. water	1/4 tsp mace
breadcrumbs	1/4 tsp grains of paradise
1/2 tsp cinnamon	salt and pepper
1/4 tsp ginger	

Lacking grains of paradise, substitute cardomom.

1. Grind breadcrumbs quite small
2. Soak in vinegar and water for 10 minutes or more
3. Add spices and whisk thoroughly

Squirrel for Those with More

PREHEAT OVEN: 350 degrees F

4 cut up squirrels   1 chopped onion
 —hind legs and meaty back pieces   4 tbsp. salt
1 chopped green pepper   1 tsp meat tenderizer
2 tbsp butter   1 tsp pepper
4 tbsp red wine   1 C. flour
1 can cream of mushroom soup   Crisco and cooking oil
1/4 C. vinegar

1. Mix vinegar, 4 tbsp salt, and enough water to cover squirrel and let sit for 2 hours
2. Mix together 1/2 tsp salt and 1/2 tsp sugar
3. Remove pieces and shake on salt/sugar mixture and pepper
4. Roll in flour
5. Fry meat in Crisco until brown, then place in baking dish.
6. Saute onion and pepper in butter
7. Add wine and soup, mix well, and pour over squirrel. Bake for 30 minutes

For a medieval dish, of course, the green peppers need to be removed or replaced with a vegetable available in that time—maybe leeks or parsnips. And the mushroom soup would need to be made as mushrooms in a white sauce. And there would be no meat tenderizer.

Shawn as Brom the Minstrel

A monk in a gray robe stopped before Shawn. "You think she knows about military preparations?" came Niall's voice in modern English.

Shawn strummed a chord, and murmured back, "Bruce told me to use my gift."

"For information."

The girl glanced at him again, and this time, gave him a fleeting smile.

"Judging by the come-hither looks over the shoulder, she knows plenty about the men around here, and half of them are military." Shawn let his fingers drift over a simple melody he'd once known quite well on guitar. It sounded all right on a lute, he decided—at least on a lute tuned like a guitar. More or less.

"Do your job."

"I could do it better if you'd get out of here. Having a monk hanging around is like having my grandmother in the back seat on a date." He strummed another chord and added in a soft undertone, "Plan on meeting her tonight as Brom. I'll be meeting someone else."

Niall glided away.

Shawn began singing another song. Something about mushrooms. Gathering mushrooms. He sang it in English, played an interlude, and sang it again in modern Gaelic, all the time watching the girl. A man at arms approached her, leaning close, touching her arm. She laughed, leaning into him, and turned quickly, moving away to another stall. She glanced back over her shoulder at Shawn, and her eyes darted away...

History

We do not have records of mushroom recipes in England and France until the 1400s, although Spain and Italy had recipes using them centuries earlier, and Hildegard spoke to their health qualities, or lack thereof, in Germany in the 1100s.

This doesn't mean the English and French never ate mushrooms in those years. Some foods—or rather the recipes for them—were considered to be common knowledge, and therefore, there was no need to use valuable parchment and ink—not so easy to come by then, as now —to write down what everyone knew anyway.

Since Shawn sings about mushrooms, however, I'll give a recipe from *Libre sent sovi,* the Spanish cookbook from 1324.

Mushroom Sauce

The Book of Sent Sovi tells the medieval Catalonian cook to mix onion, parsley, vinegar, and spices with vinegar and a little water, then put the mushroom pieces in the sauce or grill them with salt and oil. Try this:

3 C. mushrooms	1-1/2 tsp parsley
1 small onion	1/2 C. red wine vinegar
1/2 C. water	

As with many medieval recipes, it is anybody's guess what spices were used. Likely, they changed with location, season, and an individual cook and the cook's mood. Try the powder fort. Try the powder douce. Try the 8 essential spices in various combinations. Have fun!

Mushroom Sauce with Red Wine

2 tbsp unsalted butter	2 tbsp cornstarch
5 cloves garlic	1/4 C. cold water
1 small onion, chopped	1/4 C. heavy cream
8 oz. sliced mushrooms	1/4 C. grated Romano cheese
1 C. white wine	1/4 C. grated Parmesan cheese
1 C. chicken broth	

1. Melt butter in a pan over medium heat
2. Brown garlic in hot butter, about 5 minutes.
3. Mash garlic and stir into butter
4. Add onion; saute until translucent
5. Stir in mushrooms; cooking until slightly brown, 5 minutes.
6. Pour in heavy cream, stirring continually
7. Add cheeses; cook until cheese melts, 5 to 10 minutes
8. Add wine; cook until liquid is reduced by half, 5 to 10 minutes
9. Add chicken broth, bring to a simmer
10. Cook until slightly reduced, about 5 minutes.
11. Mix water and cornstarch until cornstarch is dissolved
12. Stir into mushroom sauce in the skillet, stirring regularly, until sauce thickens, 5 to 10 minutes.

Shawn in the Orchards

He jogged to the single gate leaving the castle compound. He had to get out before MacDougall came through. He had only to get past the orchards beyond, and through the next gate, and he'd be in the town's narrow, twisting streets, with plenty of places to hide.

A flurry of light, feminine voices stopped him. He picked up the collective note of agitation. Past experience told him he might well be the target. He glanced behind—back inside the castle walls—and before —across the bridge where he'd be exposed. He couldn't see them. He ran for it, the lute thumping on his back, and just as they emerged from the twilight, at the far end of the orchard, he threw himself to the right, into the shadows of the west orchard. Their voices came to him.

"It seems he's met every one of us here!" That was Emeline.

Shawn pressed a hand to his eyes, stifling a groan. Not now, Emeline!

"He'll be playing at the castle for the commander's dinner." That was Duraina.

The voices came closer. "There's only one way in and out," said the carpenter's daughter. "He's met all of you here. He'll be back to meet me. Let's wait."

...

Harclay waited in the castle courtyard to meet MacDougall personally. There were rumors he was in a black mood these days— something about a prisoner escaping his gallows, and a false accusation against the young Niall Campbell, resulting in public humiliation. The Scots would be at Carlisle sooner or later, and he'd as soon not have to deal with MacDougall's moods, as they discussed the anticipated attack.

He greeted the lord as he rode in from the orchards. Reaching a hand on his reins, he said, "Welcome, My Lord! There's a fine meal being laid even now for you and your men, and I've a wonderful lutar for you, only recently arrived!"

As he dismounted, MacDougall smiled.

A good start, Harclay thought irritably. He disliked having to soothe grown men's tempers.

"A lutar and an orchard full of comely young lasses," MacDougall said. "It seems my stay will be pleasant indeed."

"My Lord?" Harclay questioned. "Lasses in my orchard?"

Hildegard of Bingen on Apples

The apple tree is hot and moist, of such great moisture that it would flow forth if not constrained by the heat. A person young or old who suffers fogginess in his eyes should take the leaves of the apple tree in springtime, before it produces fruit for that year. He should pound the leaves to express sap and add to that an equal measure of drops flowing from a grapevine. Put them in a metal jar and at night moisten his eyelids and eyes with a feather dipped in it.

For headache or pain from illness of liver of spleen, bad humors of the belly: take the first shoots of the apple tree and place them in olive oil. Warm them in a jar in the sun. Drink it often on going to bed, to reduce the headache.

For pain in the shoulders, loins, or stomach: take earth from around the root of the apple tree, when the blossoms first come out in springtime. Heat the dirt on fire. This warmed dirt, placed on the painful place, will bring relief.

Emplumeus (Cooked Apples)

Du fait de cuisine and *Libre del Coch* both describe cooked apples, called *emplumeus of apples*. *Du fait de cuisine* recommends barberine apples, while *Libre del Coch* speaks more generally of the sweetest of apples. As is typical, neither specifies amounts—according to how much you want to make, and as much as you know you'll need, being as their measurements of choice. *Du fait de cusine* is very clear on the dishes, though—they should be of gold and silver. I guess that rules out *emplumeus* for me!

Both call for almonds—the first being clear the almonds must be ground in a mortar which does *not* smell of garlic. Other advice—it must be boiled over clean coals without smoke.

Both call for sugar—a great amount—while only *Libre del coch* uses cinnamon.

And so...emplumeus

4 apples   1/4 tsp salt
3 C. water   pinch saffron (optional)
2 C. blanched almonds   2 tsp rosewater (optional)
1/4 C. sugar

1. Peel, core, and slice apples.
2. Bring water to a boil, then add slices
3. Cook until soft, then strain, reserving liquid.
4. Chop apples into small pieces
5. Grind almonds well and place in a bowl
6. Add reserved liquid; steep for 15 minutes, stirring occasionally
7. Pour through a fine sieve into a pan with the apples
8. Add remaining ingredients and simmer until thick. Serve hot.

As long as Harclay has a whole orchard full of apples (and, much to his surprise, young maidens!) let's give his cooks a few more apple dishes to make, similar, but each a little different.

Applemoyse

3 C. apple sauce   1/2 tsp cinnamon
3/4 C. sugar   1/2 tsp. ginger
3 egg yolks

1. Mix ingredients in a pan
2. Heat until it starts to boil and thickens

Apple Muse

Take Appelys an sethe hem, an Serge hem thorwe a Sefe in-to a potte;
thanne take Almaunde Mylke & Hony, an caste ther-to, an gratid Brede,
Safroun, Saunderys, & Salt a lytil, & caste all in the potte & lete hem
sethe; & loke that thou stere it wyl, & serue it forth.
~ Harleian manuscripts

2 apples   1 tsp sandalwood
1 C. almond milk   pinch saffron
4 tbsp honey   dash of salt
1 C. bread crumbs

1. Peel, core, and slice apples.
2. Boil until soft, then press through a sieve.
3. Add almond milk, honey, bread crumbs, saffron, sandalwood, and salt and simmer.

Sorcha's Cave

They waited while the wind sloughed down the valley, rippling their cloaks. The ponies shook their manes in irritation, and bent to tasting the frosted grass. "Is this going to be some bent, old snaggle-tooth with scraggly gray hair?" Shawn asked. "Should we collect some eye of newt for her?" The light flickered in the cave entrance.

"Berries would be more appreciated." Niall scanned the foliage. Spotting a bush spangled in dark blue, he picked handfuls, dropping them into the folds of his plaid.

Shawn helped.

"'Tis Sorcha you've found."

They turned to the thin voice drifting down the hillside.

A figure stood at the cave entrance. "Come up."

Shawn took a last handful of berries, and followed Niall up a narrow dirt track wending up the hill. The woman took shape as they approached. She wore bundles of nondescript clothing. Her face, beneath the folds of the arisaid covering her head, lacked the wizened features he'd expected. She had round, rosy cheeks and bright blue eyes shining with humor. "I've little use for eye of newt," she said.

Shawn stared, uncomprehending.

Niall chuckled. "Surely you've learned by now how sound carries up the hills?"

"It was a jest," Shawn muttered.

Niall nudged him, and he added, "My apologies."

"Accepted," Sorcha said. "Come in from the cold." She led them in, edging past the fire burning at the entrance. A large cast iron pot hung over it. "It holds only turnips," she assured him, and pointed to furs on the floor and bowls on a ledge carved in the rock. "You're welcome to food and shelter. I'd think you'd not be wanting to travel further with night coming on."

"Thank you." Niall seated himself on a fur, as did Shawn. Sorcha pulled the arisaid off her head, revealing dark hair wrapped in a heavy braid. Firelight played over her ivory skin. "You seem young to be a wise woman," he said.

She laughed, dishing stew from the pot into bowls. "Age and wisdom are not always related. Though I never claimed to be wise. 'Tis others say so. If I've helped anyone, 'tis God working through me."

Shawn was about to snort—his usual response to mention of God. Niall's hard stare stopped him.

Sorcha paused, the ladle over a bowl. She peered at their identical faces. "Brothers?" she asked. "Twins?"

"Not quite," Shawn said dryly.

She peered more closely at him. "You don't believe?"

"Believe what? Are we talking God? I believe I make my own destiny." But he dropped his gaze, unnerved by her scrutiny. Her eyes seemed to prod through his skin.

"Aye, we're both doing well at that." Niall's voice crackled with sarcasm.

Shawn glared at him. "My talents are my own doing and hard work."

Sorcha tipped broth into the bowl, handed it to him, and reached for a second bowl. "You've worked hard, no doubt. Yet you came to me."

"He thought you might know something." Shawn stared at the stew, and swirled it a little. It looked better than much of what he'd eaten in this time. He lifted his wooden spoon.

"Did your mother teach you no manners?" Niall asked as he accepted the second bowl. "Prayers."

Sorcha finished spooning up her own meal and sat down on a fur, bowing her head, and saying grace.

"My mother tried," Shawn said, when she finished. "I found I got more out of life without them."

Niall snorted. "Like Amy's undying love and devotion, aye?"

Only the pure in heart can make a good soup.
~ Ludwig van Beethoven

Okay, so Beethoven isn't exactly medieval. But he's a musician, and so are Shawn and Niall. It seems curious that Beethoven would be quoted on the subject of soup, but the story is that he said it regarding his dismissal of an otherwise good housekeeper, for telling a lie—one to spare his feelings, interestingly.

I believe there's truth to the idea that the attitude with which we meet our daily tasks, no matter how small, does shine through. What we do with purity of heart and generosity of spirit, will always have a quality that other works do not.

Moreover, one Beethoven quote leads nicely into another that has nothing to do with food, but seems appropriate to this scene anyway:

Nothing is more intolerable than to have to admit to yourself your own errors.
~ Ludwig van Beethoven

Vegetables in Medieval Europe

Vegetables were so common, and so simple to prepare in medieval Europe that even cookbooks often didn't record recipes for them. Vellum and parchment were not as easy to come by as our paper, so why waste them writing down what was considered to be common knowledge?

The available vegetables were largely what we have today—asparagus, beets (roots and tops), brussel sprouts, cabbage, capers, celery —often referred to as wild celery—chard, chickpeas, cress, cucumbers, garlic, gherkins, leeks, scallions, green onions, mushrooms, mustard greens, olives, onions, parsnips, peas, radishes, spinach, squash, turnips, and white turnips.

Many varieties of beans were known—the broadbean, haricot, hairy vetch, the sweet vetch, and the most common, the fava, but not our modern green bean. There were salad greens, but no iceberg lettuce. Cauliflower was used more starting in the late Renaissance.

Some vegetables were available, but different from our modern varieties. Carrots, for instance, were smaller, and either red or white. They had gourds, but not our American pumpkin.

Highland Herbs

There are few actual recipes left of any turnip stew or turnip pottage, because the fact is, pottage or any stew mostly involved throwing in whatever food was available and letting it boil or simmer over the fire. For Sorcha, she would have had turnips in her 'pottage,' maybe onions, and maybe some herbs. Poorer people would have had parsley, sage, rosemary, and thyme. (Sound familiar? I think I'm beginning to understand something of the song!) Being of a lower economic class, not to mention living in a cave, Sorcha almost certainly did not have spices. But she would have had a wealth of herbs to gather. There are many that grow in the Highlands, and she certainly would have known them and used them.

Most of these herbs have medicinal qualities, in addition to culinary value. Wild marjoram, also known as Scots oregano, wild liquorice also known as vetch, meadowsweet, and wild garlic are several. Therefore, we'll add marjoram, garlic, and a little anise to recreate the mild licorice flavor of vetch. In fact, Sorcha certainly would have added vetch to either her stew, or drinks, for Niall or Shawn, as one of its properties is that it keeps hunger at bay on long journeys, which they were in the middle of, when they visited her.

So Sorcha's stew might have tasted something like this:

Sorcha's Turnip Pottage

water as needed	1 tsp marjoram and/or oregano
2 turnips and/or 2 leeks	1/2 tsp garlic
1 onion	1 tsp anise
1/2 C. mushrooms	wild mushrooms
1 tsp parsley	3 parsnips

1. Simmer all day over a low fire OR
2. Simmer for 30 to 60 minutes or however long you feel like on your stove

Vegetable Stew

Here's another potential recipe.

1 tbsp virgin olive oil	1 bay leaf
1 onion chopped	salt and pepper to taste
2 garlic cloves, minced	6 oz. curly kale
1-1/2 lbs leeks, sliced	1 tbsp walnut oil
1 lb turnips	1/3 C. toasted walnuts, chopped
6 C. water or vegetable stock	

1. Peel and slice turnips; stem and wash kale
2. Heat olive oil over medium heat in a pot, and add onion
3. Cook and stir until tender
4. Add leeks, stirring until softened
5. Stir in garlic
6. Add turnips, water, bay leaf, and salt, and bring to a boil
7. Reduce heat, simmer 45 to 60 minutes.
8. Remove the bay leaf.
9. While soup simmers, blanch kale in boiling salted water until tender, then transfer to cold water, drain, and squeeze out water.
10. Slice kale into think slivers. Add walnut oil and toss
11. For the modern reader, you may puree the soup in a blender. For the medieval reader, I guess this isn't going to happen, and therefore the 'same' soup is going to be quite different. The modern reader should then strain the soup, return it to the pot, and heat it through, stirring.
12. On serving, garnish with spoonfuls of greens and a sprinkling of walnuts.

Clava Cairns

Amy clutched the blanket. The whole place had an eerie stillness to it; magic and mystery quivered in the air. Wind sloughed through the pines, setting needles to rustling and whispering. Mist twisted around their ankles. Standing stones rose, wraith-like, from the gloam. Amy shivered. Someone could easily slide through time in such a place.

Angus nodded toward one of the cairns. "Let's have that coffee until it's light enough to see."

They entered the cairn, down a long, narrow passage. Stone walls rose on either side, but its roof had long since disappeared, leaving it open to the sky, and snowflakes dancing above.

Angus laid the tarp on the chilly ground and helped Amy lower herself. With their backs against the stone wall, he took out the thermos and biscuits.

"It feels sacrilegious." She wrapped her hands around the thermos. "Wasn't it a grave of some sort?"

"A thousand years ago, maybe," he said. "They've never found any bodies. Some doubt they were graves after all. They're aligned with the sun, see. I'm surprised no one else is here on the solstice."

"Maybe they're all down at Stonehenge."

They fell quiet. She laid her head on his shoulder, and dozed. Shawn prowled her dreams, Shawn in the midst of stones, circling, looking to the sky, reaching for home. She had no idea if it was the stone circle by the cairn.

Coffee

16 oz. powder non-dairy creamer	1/4 C. sugar (adjust to taste)
3/4 C. instant decaffeinated coffee	1 1/2 tsp cinnamon
	1 C. brown sugar

1. Mix all ingredients together
2. Store in an airtight container until used

Scottish Parliament Cakes (Parlies)

PREHEAT OVEN: 325 degrees F

These biscuits have a Scottish and historical significance, as they were first made at the Luckie Fykie, a shop in Edinburgh, for members of Parliament.

2-1/2 C. plain flour	1 egg
4 oz. butter	2 tbsp molasses
2 tbsp brown sugar	2 tsp ground ginger

1. Mix flour, ginger and sugar
2. Melt butter in a pan; add molasses
3. Bring to a boil, stirring continuously
4. Turn off heat; add other ingredients, mixing vigorously
5. When cooled, scoop up small amounts of mixture with a dessert spoon and drop onto a well greased baking tray or sheet.
6. Flatten with a fork, leaving room for all to spread
7. Bake 25 to 30 minutes.
8. Remove biscuits from tray; store in an air-tight container.

Mairi's Christmas Cookies and Hot Chocolate

I sink happily into lazy days of naps and board games and walks to a small pub for hot chocolate with Gavin and Hamish. Mairi admonishes them to quiet down, and stop pestering me. But I like their energy. They remind me of my young cousins, playing football with Shawn and jumping for the gifts he brought them. They keep my mind off the professor with my crucifix, our failed searches, and the question of what now? Mairi is motherly, baking, splotches of flour on cheeks and elbows, hugging her sons, laughing with red cheeks, and forever pushing back a dark curl that insists on falling over one eye. She assures me she is there to listen, but doesn't pry.

Scottish Shortbread

PREHEAT OVEN: 350 degrees F

1 lb butter

4 C. all-purpose flour
1 C. granulated sugar

1. Let butter soften to room temperature; beat in a large bowl until smooth
2. Blend sugar in well
3. Add flour cup by cup. Dough should be very stiff
4. Spread into 9 x 13" baking pan, pressing evenly on all edges, and pricking vent holes across top of dough
5. Bake 45 to 60 minutes until golden brown
6. Remove from oven, cut into 2" pieces, and cool in pan

Hot Chocolate

1 C. milk
1/3 C. white sugar
1 pinch salt
1 tsp vanilla extract

2 tbsp sweetened cocoa powder
2 oz. semisweet baking chocolate
1 C. heavy cream

1. Heat milk in a small pan over low heat until it begins to steam
2. Add sugar, cocoa powder, vanilla extract, and salt, stirring briskly until dissolved
3. Break chocolate into pieces and stir in until melted
4. Remove pan from heat, and allow to cool a little
5. Beat cream in large bowl, using an electric mixer, until stiff peaks form
6. Fold whipped cream into hot chocolate

Brown Sugar Spiced Shortbread Cookies

PREHEAT OVEN: 325 degrees F

1 1/4 C. all-purpose flour
3 tbsp brown sugar

1 tbsp white sugar
1/2 tsp ground cinnamon

1. Combine flour, brown sugar, white sugar, cinnamon
2. Mix in butter until the batter is fine crumbs
3. Pack crumbs into a ball and knead until smooth
4. Roll dough out on a floured surface to an 8 inch circle
5. Transfer dough to a baking sheet
6. Slice into 16 wedges while singing *Will the circle be a broken...* The answer is *No!* Do not break the circle!
7. Bake 25 minutes, until center has set
8. Cut into wedges again while the shortbread is still warm
9. Cool on a wire rack

Christmas at Glenmirril

Glenmirril closed in on them for the winter. It wasn't the stark existence Shawn had dreaded. The walls felt safe, tall and imposing, shutting out enemies and the loch's chilling winds. Torches and blazing hearths gave heat and cheerful light to every room. Tapestries appeared on the walls for warmth, filling the castle with vibrant colors. Adam's widow stopped before them with her daughters, pointing up, telling the stories woven into them. Garlands and extra candles decked the great hall for the season of Christ Mass.

Here is the refrain and just some of the verses of the traditional carol, *Here We Go A-Wassailing.*

Here we come a-wassailing
Among the leaves so green
Here we come a-wandering
So fair to be seen

Our wassail cup is made
of the rosemary tree
And so is your beer
of the best barley

Call up the butler of this house,
Put on his golden ring.
Let him bring us up a glass of beer,
And better we shall sing

Bring us out a table
And spread it with a cloth;
Bring us out a mouldy cheese,
And some of your Christmas loaf.

Wassail

Although most people know the song, how many have made or tasted wassail? Nicholas Culpeper left us a recipe from 1620. *Wassail* comes from the Anglo-Saxon *be whole,* which was their equivalent of *Good health to you!*

PREHEAT OVEN: 375 degrees F

2 or 3 cinnamon sticks	4 apples
3 blades of mace	4 oz. of sugar
4 cloves	1/2 pt of brown ale
1 tsp of nutmeg	1/2 pt of cider
1 ginger root	

1. Core apples; sprinkle with sugar and water and bake for 30 minutes, until tender
2. Mix ale, cider, and spices and heat without boiling
3. Leave for 30 minutes
4. Put roasted apples in a punch bowl
5. Strain cider and pour over apples

Notice the three spices in this—cloves, nutmeg, and ginger. This is a common trio, on which Hildegard had definite ideas—as we will see when Amy goes to Honora's crumbling old manor above the pounding sea, and has Hildegard's *Cookies of Joy* (**p. 206**)

Sing a song of sixpence
A pocket full of rye
Four and twenty blackbirds
Baked in a pie

When the pie was opened
The birds began to sing
Wasn't that a dainty dish
To set before the king?

The History

It's not just a nursery rhyme. It really was done! While the earliest record we have of this rhyme dates only to 1744, it is believed to be much older than that, due to a line in the 1614 tragic-comedy, *Bonduca:* "Whoa, here's a stir now! Sing a song o' sixpence!" Even further back, in 1602, Shakespeare's *Twelfth Night* refers to sixpence for a song.

Even apart from the poem, we know live birds in a pie really was 'a thing.' An Italian cookbook from 1549 tells us how to "make pies so that birds may be alive in them and file out when it is cut up." It is recorded that songbirds flew out of a pie at the wedding banquet of Marie de' Medici and Henry IV of France in 1600. Maestro Martino da Como's cookbook *Libro de Arte Coquinaria*, published between 1450 and 1460, has a recipe for 'flying pie.'

Live Bird Pie

Subtleties, as noted earlier, were a beloved medieval tradition at feasts. For Glenmirril's Christmas feast, we know from Niall's memories in another scene, there was, at least once, a subtlety of birds within birds. But there might also have been a pie opened to loose dozens of songbirds lifting into flight, rising above the heads of astonished and delighted guests, as they flapped and swooped and sang around the Great Hall.

The Non-Recipe

Modern readers question how birds can fly out of a baked pie, alive and well and singing. It is a true case of, *No birds were harmed in the making of this pie.* It's really rather ingenious, in my humble opinion.

1. Make a regular sized pie of your choice (or, preferably the king's choice)
2. Make a very large empty pie shell is made, its sides higher than the small pie, with a hole in the bottom at least big enough for the small pie to fit through
3. Fill it with flour (or in other directions, beans) to keep its shape during cooking
4. When it is cooked, open the hole in the bottom and remove the flour
5. Lift the small pie in through the hole on the bottom
6. Immediately before serving, put the small birds in the empty space around the small pie
7. Serve it forth! As so many medieval cookbooks say!

Singing birds! Perhaps this was why he was called Maestro!

Blancmange Chicken

White broth: Take capons, chickens killed before their time, either in their entirety or broken into halves or quarters, and pieces of veal. Cook them with pork in water and vinegar. When they are cooked, take the almonds and peel and boil them and mix them with your chicken broth. When it is very clear and free of deposits and you have strained it, take white ginger, trimmed or peeled, and grains of paradise, as made above, and strain it well, and combine it with the almond milk. And if it is not thick enough, mix with starch or rice that has been boiled, and then add a taste of verjuice and add in white sugar in great abundance. And when you are ready to serve it, pour over it a spice that is called red coriander, and place sugared pomegranate seeds and fried almonds around the edge of the bowl.
~ *Le Menagier de Paris,* 1393

1 chicken breast	1/4 tsp ginger
6-8 oz. of veal	1/4 tsp grains of paradise
1 C. uncooked rice	1 to 2 tbsp red wine
1/2 C. ground almonds	1 tbsp butter
3 C. chicken stock	1/2 tsp lemon juice or verjuice
2 tsp sugar	

1. Poach chicken and veal in water and red wine
2. Cover rice with water and set aside for 15 minutes
3. Cover almonds with stock and set aside for 15 minutes
4. Drain rice; add chicken and almond/broth mixture
5. Add a tbsp of butter, lemon juice or verjuice, and spices, and cook, stirring frequently until rice is tender

Leche Frys in Lentoun (Almond Milk Fruit Pie)

*Leche frys in lentoun. Drawe a thik almaunde mylke wiþ water. Take
dates and pyke hem clene with apples and peeres, & mynce hem with
prunes damysyns; take out þe stones out of þe prunes, & kerue the
prunes a two. Do þerto raisouns, coraunce, sugur, flour of canel, hoole
macys and clowes, gode powdours & salt; colour hem vp with saundres.
Meng þise with oile. Make a coffyn as þou didest bifore & do þis fars
þerin, & bake it wel, and serue it forth.*
~ 14th century, *Forme of Cury*

PREHEAT OVEN: 375 degrees F

2 C. thick almond milk	1/2 tsp each cinnamon, mace, cloves
1/4 C. chopped dates	1/4 tsp each ginger, nutmeg
2 apples	1/4 tsp white pepper
2 pears	1/4 tsp salt
1/4 C. pitted prunes	a small amount of red sandalwood*
1/4 C. currants	2 tbsp olive oil
1/4 C. raisins	pie shell
3 tbsp sugar	

*Red sandalwood was used mainly as a coloring agent by medieval
cooks. If you go for authentic, make sure you get red sandalwood. A
few drops of red food dye will serve the same purpose.

1. Peel, core, and slice the apples and pears
2. Mix well: almond milk, sugar, spices, oil, and sandalwood (or
   red dye) until milk is bright red
3. Mix fruits separately, add milk and sugar mixture, mix well, and
   put in pie shell
4. Bake 45 minutes, until filling is set and the top is golden brown

At the pub with Helen

"What's less well known," Helen added, "is that Columba went on to Glenmirril. Are you familiar with it?"

"Very." Amy felt Angus's eyes on her.

"Fascinating place. People see things there. I'd not go in it at night." Helen shuddered. "That American musician who disappeared, now, they said he spent the night there and wasn't the same afterward. Not the first time I've heard that sort of thing."

"Really?" The baby chose that moment to kick hard. Amy gasped, laughed, touched her stomach.

"Due soon?" Helen smiled at Angus.

"Six weeks." He smiled at Amy, his eyes reflecting the tiny candle flame dancing on the table. "Columba, Glenmirril?" He squeezed Amy's hand under the table.

"Yes. He stayed there a few weeks." Helen returned to her narrative. That lord, too, was converted, and so enthusiastic that he demanded Columba send back monks to nurse his newborn faith to maturity. Through the years, as the wooden stockade gave way to stone walls, and the fortress grew into a motte and bailey castle, as children were born and grew and died, the monks were as much a part of castle life as the hills and loch. As more revelers sought the warmth of the pub, and the noise grew, Helen leaned forward, recounting miracles and prophecies of Columba and his monks at Glenmirril. "A few centuries later," she finished, "a lord granted them land, across Loch Ness, but they never forgot their roots with Columba." "I haven't found any of this on the internet," Amy said. "No, you wouldn't," Helen replied. Angus raised a hand, summoning a waitress. "Something to eat?" he asked Amy. Amy blinked at the noisy pub, so engrossed had she become in Columba's miracles, in the loch and hills and life of Glenmirril. "Anything for you, Helen?" Angus asked.

"Oh, fish pie?" Helen looked around as Angus ordered, seeming as surprised as Amy to find herself in the pub.

Fish Pie

PREHEAT OVEN: 335 degrees F

1 C. fish stock
1 C. milk, 2 tbsp milk
1-1/2 C. fish (salmon, cod, haddock)
1 bay leaf
5 1/2 C. creamed mashed potatoes
2 oz. butter
1 tsp nutmeg

white of 1 leek, washed and finely sliced
2 oz. all-purpose flour
1 tbsp finely chopped fresh parsley
salt and pepper
grated cheddar cheese

1. Whisk together fish stock and milk; bring to a simmer
2. Add fish and bay leaf; poach for 5 minutes
3. Remove fish, saving stock and milk
4. In a pan, saute sliced leeks in butter until leeks are soft
5. Stir flour in well, add stock and milk, stirring, and raise heat
6. Cook until sauce thickens slightly, then turn off heat
7. Remove bay leaf; add fish, parsley, salt and pepper and pour it all into a casserole dish
8. Cover with mashed potatoes and sprinkle with grated cheese
9. Bake 20 to 30 minutes, until sauce bubbles under potatoes

Carol Sees Bruce's Ring

Carol gazes out the window at the passing countryside. Just as I stayed, to be near Shawn and Niall, it means everything to her simply to be here, where her son was, where she hopes he still is. I can't tell her he is indeed here. Just not in this century. I hate withholding information. But I can't tell this insane story to a grieving mother.

A ham and noodle casserole waits in the crock pot at home. She smiles. "Did you know this is my favorite?"

"I remember Shawn going out of his way to make it for you once." I serve up rich creamy noodles while she pours us water. I join her as she prays over her meal.

Lifting her head, she says, "You said you and Angus were working on a different angle." I stare at my hands, not knowing what to say, and revert to the nervous habit of twisting my ring.

"How unusual." Carol's heightened pitch breaks through my quest for a sane answer.

I glance up. She's reaching to touch the red stone. Panic flutters in my heart.

"You always wear such delicate jewelry. Can I see it?"

I can't think of a reason to say no. With shaky hands, I slide it off my finger and push it across the table. Carol studies the wide gold band. "Where did you get it?"

"Shawn." I clear my throat. "Shawn gave it to me."

Carol squints at the inscription inside. "Robert the Bruce?" She looks up. "Of Bannockburn fame?"

I nod guiltily, furiously wishing I'd learned anything from Shawn about making up stories.

Shawn's Favorite Ham and Noodle Casserole

PREHEAT OVEN: 350 degrees F

16 oz egg noodles
1 1/2 C. of diced ham
2 tbsp shredded Parmesan cheese
1 tbsp of melted butter
Topping:
2 tbsp of melted butter
1/4 C. of grated cheese (any kind)
1/4 C. of bread crumbs

Sauce:
2 C. of sour cream
3/4 C. of milk
1 1/2 tbsp of salt
1/2 tbsp of pepper
1 tbsp parsley flakes

1. Cook and drain noodles
2. In buttered casserole dish, mix cooked noodles with ham, Parmesan cheese and melted butter
3. In two *separate* bowls combine sauce ingredients and topping ingredients
4. Pour sauce over noodles and stir.
5. Sprinkle with topping. Bake, uncovered for 30 to 40 minutes,

Meeting Christina in the Stables

He leaned against the stall door. "Old MacDonald wouldn't approve, would he?" he asked the pony. The animal slurped from its water trough, ignoring him. "Come on." He patted its rump. "Give me a neigh-neigh here or a neigh-neigh there, anything to let me know you're not really ignoring me. 'Cause it looks to me like you are."

The animal shook its mane.

"You know, I'm Shawn Kleiner. Nobody ignored me." Despite the chill in the air, he'd worked hard and was hot. He yanked his vest off, standing in his bell-sleeved shirt. "Or should I say, nobody *will* ignore me in seven hundred years."

The animal chomped its hay.

"Work those boys hard!" Shawn imitated MacDonald. "If you're soft on them now, 'twill go harder on them in battle." His stomach rumbled. The smells of venison and pigeon pie and bread warm from the ovens came from the great hall, across the bailey and through the gate. Niall's place would be empty at the head table, waiting for Shawn to fill it. He didn't want to be Niall. He wanted, just for a few minutes, to be himself, even if it was only with a pony who ignored him. At least nobody was calling him Sir Niall.

A rustle at the door drew his attention. In the dim light, a slender woman led in a black mare. It was Christina. Shawn drew back into the shadows. She led the horse to its stall, singing softly to it.

Shawn smiled. Amy would do the same thing. But a twinge of guilt followed quickly on the private pleasure of listening to her sing. She wouldn't like to know she was being watched. He stepped out of the shadows. "Hey."

She spun, and on seeing him, moved quickly to the door. "Red will see to the hay."

Shawn laughed. At her blank look, he realized she had no idea why he was laughing. "Hey." He spelled it. "It's what we say in my—um, country—for hello. Not what horses eat."

She smiled, and he liked her all the more for laughing at herself.

Fowles in the frith, medieval song

Fowles in the frith, birds/woods
The fisshes in the flood,
And I mon waxe wood must go mad
Much sorwe I walke with
For beste of boon and blood. Bone

Pigeon Pie

Season your pigeons with peper, saffron, cloves and mace, with vergis
and salt, then put them into your paest and so close them vp, and bake
them, these will bake in halfe an houre then take them forth and if ye
thynke them drye take a litle vergis and butter and put to them and so
serue them.
~ 1545, A Propre new booke of Cokery

PREHEAT OVEN: 350 degrees F

5 pigeons	1/2 C. beef broth
1/4 tsp pepper	2 tbsp red wine
1/4 tsp cloves	2 tbsp verjuice
1/4 tsp mace	salt
1/2 C. diced onions	2 tbsp butter
5 mushrooms, diced	pastry

1. Remove pigeon meat from bones and dice
2. Saute onions and meat in butter about 5 minutes
3. Add mushrooms, saute another minute, and add spices
4. Add beef broth, red wine, and verjuice and simmer 10 minutes
5. Put pastry in pie pan and fill with pigeon mixture
6. Cover with more pastry and crimp edges closed
7. Bake for 30 to 40 minutes
8. When done, the top of the pie should sound hollow when tapped
9. Remove from oven and cool

Venison Stewed in Red Wine and Ginger

Wel ende edelike spijse, a 15th century coookbook, advises that the venison be cut into pieces, well larded, cooked in a lot of wine and a little water with chopped bacon and 'sufficient'saffron, ginger, and cinnamon.

2 lbs venison steak	1 tsp cinnamon
6 slices bacon	1 tsp ginger
2-1/4 C. red wine	a pinch of ground saffron
1 C. water	breadcrumbs

1. Dice venison and cut bacon into small pieces
2. Put into a pot with all other inredients
3. Bring to a boil, then simmer for 20 minutes
4. For a sauce, strain the cooking broth and thicken with breadcrumbs

Warm Bread

This interesting type of bread comes from *Eenen Nyeuwen cooc boeck,* 1560:

PREHEAT OVEN: 400 degrees F

2 C. whole wheat flour	1 tbsp. fennel seed
2 C. white flour	1-1/8 C. lukewarm water
4 tbsp. honey	1/3 lb diced bacon
1-1/2 tsp salt	4 tsp dry yeast
2 tbsp. soft butter	

1. Fry bacon, drain, and dice very small
2. Mix yeast, salt, fennel seeds, white flour, and wheat flour
3. Mix honey into warm water and add to flour and kneed well
4. Set in a bowl, cover with a moist cloth and let rise in a warm place for 45 minutes
5. Add bacon, knead again, shape into a round; let rise 30 minutes
6. Bake 45 minutes

Rob Invites Himself to Dinner

Rob leans close; touches Carol's arm; speaks as if to the bereaved. "Would you like chicken? Can I pour you tea?"

He is auditioning for the role of Beloved Son. I'm embarrassed for him.

"I'm fine, Rob, thank you." She squeezes his arm back and pours her own tea. "Thank you for all you've done." She turns to Angus. "Have you seen his office?"

Angus shakes his head. "I haven't." His lips are tight.

I pray Rob won't mention my office.

Carol dishes boiled potatoes onto Rob's plate. "Angus and Amy had an idea about genealogy."

I close my eyes. No, Carol, don't.

Rob coughs into his napkin. His eyebrows shoot up. "Genealogy?" He glares at Angus, who glares back.

"Shawn's grandmother came from Skye." Carol glances between them. "They thought maybe...."

Angus reaches abruptly for the chicken.

"Did you want more?" I ask loudly. "It's good, isn't it?"

"Aye!" Angus agrees enthusiastically. "You're a grand cook, Mrs. Kleiner!"

"Call me Carol." Her cheeks glow with pleasure. "James loved to cook. It's his recipe."

Rob looks suspiciously from me to Angus. My nerves jump, praying he won't press the issue, here in front of Carol. "I'll have to get that recipe!" I reach for the carrots. "Something in the spices?" "

Oh, yes," she agrees with more enthusiasm than the question deserves. "He was a master with spices!"

Rob tries to meet my eyes. I avoid his, telling Carol, "I'm arranging Ma Vlast as a violin solo!" I lean forward, as enthralled as if I've won a new house.

"Are you?" she asks with the same out of proportion interest.

"Smetana's grand, now, is he not!" Angus declares.

"Do you even know who he is?" Rob glares at him.

Angus tries valiantly for a smile, but only manages a smirk. "The father of Czech music. He composed piano pieces, orchestral works, and operas. I particularly like his Doctor Faust."

I look down at the creamy-white potatoes on my plate, hiding a smile. I told him this when I started working on it.

"And," Angus leans forward, he shares a birthday with Dr. Seuss!"

Chicken Bonnie Prince Charlie

4 boneless skinless chicken breasts	1 oz. flaked almonds
3 tbsp Drambuie	4 apples
1/2 chicken stock	a little flour
1 C. whipping cream	salt and pepper
3 oz. butter	

1. Flour and season chicken breasts, then fry in hot butter, turning once and browning well
2. Sprinkle with Drambuie, add chicken stock, and cover
3. Simmer for ten minutes
4. Peel and core apples, cut into thick slices and cook in butter until soft
5. Remove cooked chicken to a serving dish; keep warm in the oven.
6. Make sauce by adding more Drambuie to the stock in the pan
7. Stir in cream
8. Heat without boiling, and add roasted flaked almonds
9. Cover chicken with sauce and garnish with apple slices

At Honora's

Honora sailed through the arch from the kitchen, bearing cookies steaming from the oven. "Oh, aye, the MacDougalls, thieves through and through! Always stealing our cattle." She clucked her tongue.

"Now how does anyone know whose cattle they were?" Helen's hands went to her hips.

"They were the MacDonalds' cattle," Angus said. "The question is, is Duncan of the same MacDougalls? I've no idea what other he'd be of, but then why is he at Glenmirril? Why would Christina not have gone to Creagsmalan?"

"But this can't be right," Amy objected. "If James Angus is Duncan and Christina's son, then Niall and Allene can't be Shawn's ancestors. And they have to be."

"Why?" Helen asked.

Honora set the cookies on the tea cart, saying over her shoulder, "See here, there's a question mark by Duncan MacDougall's name. There's doubt as to James Angus's paternity."

"Why would they think it was a MacDougall at all?" Amy asked, ignoring Helen's question.

"No one knows. Aye, 'tis Duncan MacDougall of Creagsmalan." Honora handed her a cookie, chirping. "Eat, eat, eat!"

"He can't be the father of a child born at Glenmirril," Angus insisted.

"But the father is in doubt," Honora reminded him. "Which is odd, for there are records of her marrying Duncan MacDougall."

"A second husband?" Helen said. "It would hardly be unusual, with war and disease, for her to be widowed and re-marry."

"Christina," Angus said around a mouthful of cookie. "Think back, Amy, to Brian's stories at Creagsmalan. Wasn't that the name of the wife chasing her husband away from the mistress? Quite the shrew?"

Amy nodded. "Yes. So maybe she married Duncan, and went back to Glenmirril after she was widowed?"

"Come to think of it," said Angus, "Remember the placard at Creagsmalan? I told you it was wrong because Duncan MacDougall was killed at Glenmirril. Before 1317."

Abernethy Biscuits

The Abernethy biscuit was created by John Abernethy in the 1700s as a digestive aid, on the premise that most diseases result from digestive disorders. It is based on hardtack, but adds sugar for energy and caraway seeds to combat gas. Carminative effect really sounds so much better, but let's just say what they do. They fight flatulence.

PREHEAT OVEN: 375 degrees F

5-1/2 C. all purpose flour	1-1/2 C. shortening
1-1/2 tsp lemon zest	3 eggs
1-1/2 C. white sugar	3 tbsp milk
1-1/2 tsp baking powder	3 tbsp caraway seed

1. Mix flour, sugar, and baking powder in a bowl
2. Cut in shortening until you have coarse crumbs
3. In another bowl, beat together eggs, milk, seeds and lemon zest
4. Add to dry ingredients and blend until smooth
5. If dough is too stiff, add extra milk, a tbsp at a time
6. Roll dough out to 1/4 inch thick on a floured surface
7. Stamp out 2" rounds with cookie cutter and set cookies 2 inches apart on greased baking sheets
8. Bake 7 to 10 minutes, until edges are lightly browned
9. Cool on wire racks

Hildegard von Bingen's Cookies of Joy

While Honora may not have known what she was serving, I can see her making these cookies, as it's a very old, and very simple recipe, created by Hildegard von Bingen for the same reasons John Abernethy created his: health. Yes, cookies for health and happiness! I like these people! Hildegard had four rules of life:

1.Strengthen the soul (through prayer and meditation, by developing talents and virtues and eliminating weakness and vice).

2.Regular detoxification through treatments designed to strengthen the body (bloodletting, fasting, purging, and more)

3.When body, soul, and mind are equally strong, there is balance in the bodily elements. This balance is easily upset by poor habits in eating, drinking, and 'lusts.'

4.Sharpen the senses (live with purpose and good cheer, love life, use your senses well, and live responsibly).

Her *Cookies of Joy*—so-called today, though likely not by her—contained ingredients she believed helped with this balance and good health.

Cookies of Joy

PREHEAT OVEN: 375 degrees F

3/4 C. butter (1-1/2 sticks)   2 C. of flour (whole wheat or spelt)
1/2 C. brown sugar   1-1/2 tsp of cinnamon
1/2 C. of white/cane sugar   1 tsp of nutmeg
1 egg—as fresh as possible   3/4 tsp of cloves
1 tsp of baking powder   Up to another tsp of each spice, to
1/4 tsp of salt   taste

1. Mix butter and sugar until fluffy
2. Mix egg in well
3. Sift dry ingredients together and..you guessed it...mix well
4. Roll dough out to 1/4 inch thick and use a cookie cutter to cut out cookies...OR roll dough into 1 inch circles, place on cookie sheet, and press flat with the bottom of a glass—do whichever makes you happiest because these are cookies of *joy!*
5. Bake 10 minutes, until edges are just starting to turn brown

Hildegard recommended bakers make and eat these frequently to 'reduce the bad humors, enrich the blood, and fortify the nerves.' I don't know about you, but I'm all for a prescription for eating cookies often! I might even say it gives me joy!

Rob and Amy Argue

Rob appeared for dinner on a regular basis. "I've got a lead in Aberdeen," he said one week, and the next, over Carol's apple-spiced pork chops, "Someone saw him in Fife. I know this one's going somewhere."

Amy pushed at her mashed potatoes with her fork. She lifted her eyes to Rob's, when Carol rose to remove brownies from the oven. They locked silently, a wordless battle, her plea not to get Carol's hopes up, and his angry rejoinder not to tell her crazy stories.

Carol turned from the sink, lines etched around her mouth. "Rob, tell me about it later. You two go to the front room while I clean up."

"He's in Fife," Amy hissed, in the front room. "He's in Aberdeen. He's supposedly all over Scotland, Rob, always just two feet ahead of you." She yanked back from his reach. "You're not going to find him!"

Mashed Potatoes

5 lbs potatoes	1/2 tsp oregano
1/2 C. butter	1-1/2 C. cream cheese
2 C. Parmesan cheese	1/2 head garlic, peeled and minced
1 C. chopped fresh chives	1 pinch salt and pepper to taste

1. Bring a pot of salted water to a boil
2. Add potatoes; cook until tender but still firm.
3. Drain and return to stove over low heat to dry for 1 to 2 minutes.
4. Add the rest of the ingredients and mash until smooth

Apple Spiced Pork Chops

8-oz. pork chops   2 C. water
1/4 tsp salt   1/4 C. firmly packed brown sugar
1/2 tsp black pepper   1 tsp ground cinnamon
1 tsp canola oil   1/2 tsp ground cloves
cooking spray   1/2 tsp ground ginger
1 3/4 C. chopped onion   5 oz. dried apples

1. Season pork with salt and pepper.
2. Heat a nonstick pan over medium-high heat, add oil and swirl to coat.
3. Cook pork until browned on each side, then put in a crockpot coated with cooking spray
4. Reduce heat to medium under pan, add onion to drippings; sauté until tender, about 3 minutes
5. Stir in 2 cups water, scraping pan to loosen pork bits
6. Stir in brown sugar, cinnamon, cloves, and ginger, and remove pan from heat
7. Add apples to slow cooker and pour onion and spice sauce over apples
8. Cover; cook on LOW for 3 to 3 1/2 hours or until tender.

Hawking Party

With a shriek, the hawk plummeted, a black silhouette against the blue winter sky, its sharp beak diving at Shawn. He yelped, threw his arms over his head, protecting himself from a flurry of wings flapping around his face, and sharp talons grappling for him.

Hugh yelled. Wings thrashed.

Shawn dropped to the ground, shouting, "Get it off me!"

Hands yanked at him, Niall shouted, and Allene said, "Get up now, Shawn, the bird is on Niall's arm."

He climbed sheepishly to his feet, looking with blazing cheeks from Christina, who stared at him in wide-eyed shock, to Brother David, who stared at the ground, his mouth small and tight against his clear attempt not to laugh.

Hugh made no such pretense, but guffawed loudly, slapping his thigh. "I've not seen aught so funny in years!" he declared.

"The thing is too stupid to know the difference between a man and a rabbit!" Shawn declared indignantly.

"The way you threw yourself on the ground, nor can I." Niall grinned, as he tugged a hood over the bird's head. He whispered soothing sounds at it.

"You're comforting that murderous thing?" Shawn demanded. "It attacked me!"

The Ballad of Chevy Chase

Before Chevy Chase was a city in Maryland or an actor, it was a hunt (the chase) in the Cheviot Hills—the rolling hills that lie in the Scottish Borders and England's Northumberland—and a very popular ballad.

Although dating to the 15th century, this song was likely carried down orally from long before that, and refers to the Battle of Otterburn in 1388 in which the then-Earl of Douglas (another James), died. A very lengthy poem, it begins thus:

> *The fattest harts in all Cheviot*
> *He would kill and carry away*
> *'By my faith' said the doughty Douglas again,*
> *'I will let that hunting if I may!'*

The Falcon, 1350s, or The Corpus Christi Carol

Lully, lulley! Lully, lulley!
The falcon hath borne my make away!
He bare him up, he bare him down,
He bare him into an orchard brown.

In that orchard there was an halle,
That was hanged with purple and pall.
And in that hall there was a bed,
And it was hanged with gold so red.

And in that bed there li'th a knight
His woundes bleeding day and night.
At that bed's foot there li'eth a hound,
Licking the blood as it runs down.

By that bed-side kneeleth a may,
And she weepeth both night and day.
And at that bed's head standeth a stone,
Corpus Christi written thereon.
Lully, lulley! Lully, lulley!
The falcon hath borne my make away!

History

Falconry was the sport of kings. Indeed, our first record of it in Britain is of Ethelbert II, the Saxon king who lived in the 700s. Falconry, however, did not involve merely falcons, but various birds of prey, trained to hunt, often in conjunction with the castle's hunting dogs, some of whom were trained specifically to work with the falcons.

In medieval times, hawking birds were allowed according to status and class. Servants and children were allowed kestrels—not considered worth much for hunting. Priests might hunt with sparrowhawks, yeomen with goshawks, and earls and barons with peregrines—females for the earls, and males for the barons. Ladies hunted with merlins. A king could have what he pleased, but gyr falcons were favored.

While falconry was a vital part of feeding the people of the castle, it was also fun sport and group event. The birds became symbols of status, power, and strength. They found their way onto coats of arms, banners, into songs, tales, and poetry, and even onto the Baeux tapestry, which features a scene of Harold Godwinson's falcon hunt.

Rabbit

Rabbit stew from *Ménagier de Paris,* 1393

1 rabbit	5 C. onions
2 tbsp lard or oil	2 tsp ginger
1 piece of toast	1/2 tsp cinnamon
1/2 C. wine	1/4 tsp nutmeg,
6 tbsp good red wine vinegar	1/4 tsp long pepper
2 C. beef or chicken stock	1/4 tsp guinea pepper
4 tbsp verjuice	a pinch of ground cloves
	2 tsp salt

1. Roast rabbit on a grill or spit, cut into pieces.
2. Cook onions over low heat in 2 tbsp of oil
3. Add rabbit meat
4. Pour in vinegar, turn up heat
5. Scrape any meat from bottom of pan and lower heat
6. Grill or toast bread, then soak with stock and wine.
7. Mix powdered spices with verjuice and add to rabbit stew
8. Simmer, covered, for 45 minutes

The Hunting Party Picnics

Brother David helped Allene spread tartans over the pebbly shore, as Hugh dug in his pony's saddle packs for bannocks and meat pies. Christina gathered berries in her cloak and re-joined them.

"Great place," Shawn commented, avoiding Niall's eyes. "I spent every summer at the loch with my dad. Fishing, swimming." He stopped. He couldn't mention water skiing. "Good times!"

Christina smiled. "Where was that?"

"In my country." He felt the glances exchanged among the others.

Niall extended a hand to Allene, and they wandered off along the shore.

Hugh cleared his throat. "Eat, Christina. We've a long ride home. Brother David, will you have ale?"

"I will." The monk drank deeply from the skin.

Christina looked from one to the other, and back to Shawn. "Tell me more of your country. You say you were wealthy, yet you didn't ride or hunt or hawk."

"I had people to do it for me." Shawn hoped his cheerful voice would dissuade her. He could make a joke of it, turn her away from the subject.

"You had men to ride for you?" she asked doubtfully. "That makes little sense."

Fruit tarts—Tartys in Applis

PREHEAT OVEN: 350 degrees F

2 apples	2 tbsp butter
2 pears	1 tsp powder douce
1/4 C. raisins	a pinch of saffron
1/4 C. dried figs	a pie crust

1. Chop and dice all fruits into small pieces
2. Mix fruit, spices, and butter well, and put it all into a pie crust
3. Bake 45 to 50 minutes until done.

Meat Pasties

PREHEAT OVEN: 350 degrees F

Pastry:

2 C. shortening

2 C. boiling water

6 C. flour

2 tsp salt

Filling:

5 carrots, peeled and diced

2 onions, chopped

2 lbs ground beef

1 lb ground pork

1 tbsp salt

2 tsp pepper

2 tsp garlic powder

1/4 C. butter

1. Stir shortening and water together until shortening is melted.
2. Gradually add flour and salt to make a soft dough
3. Cover and refrigerate for 1-1/2 hours.
4. Dice carrots and chop onions, and mix with beef, pork and seasonings
5. Divide dough into 12 equal parts. On a floured surface, roll out one portion at a time into circles approximately 6 inches across
6. Put 1/4 cup filling in the middle of each pie, top with a bit of butter.
7. Moisten edges of dough with water, fold over filling and press edges together to seal
8. Place on ungreased baking sheets and cut vent slits in the top of each
9. Bake for 1 hour, or until golden brown

Medieval Meat Pie

PREHEAT OVEN: 350 degrees F

1/2 tsp ground cardamom
1/2 to1 C. broth
1 tsp cinnamon
1 C. grated cheese
1 dash cooking wine
4 egg yolks
1/2 tsp nutmeg

1-1/2 lbs beef, pork, rabbit, and/or venison
1 onion, diced very fine
pie shell (with lid)
1/2 C. currants, raisins or any dried fruit

1. Broil meat only to very rare, but cooked through; then dice
2. Mix with all ingredients except pie shell (that would be awkward!)
3. For the broth, add only enough to make the mixture a little wetter.
4. Fill pie shell with mixture
5. Seal lid of pie, and pierce holes in the top with a knife.
6. Bake for 45 to 60 minutes, till shell is golden brown.

Amy and Angus Discuss Trek to Monadhliath

As we drive, we discuss how the blessing affects James. Do we take him along to Monadhliath, or leave him with Carol? "It draws father and son together for their protection," Angus insists. "He'll draw Shawn into our time, not the other way around, because that would be for Shawn's protection. And they need to be together, for anything to happen, aye?"

"As far as we know," I agree.

"Monadhliath is hard to get to even today," he says. "Niall and Shawn were at Carlisle, Stirling, Cambuskenneth, Creagsmalan, Northumbria. If Shawn was ever at Monadhliath, it was in June, when he and Allene may have stopped on their way to Hugh's camp. When else would they even have time to go to such a remote place?"

We conclude it's safe to take James with us in April. "So," Angus says. "That's solved. Lunch." He directs me down a highway, around a round-about, through a small town, to a pub. A dozen roses wait on the table. We celebrate my success with lemon shrimp. My heart is in my throat, feeling loved, protected, and cherished.

Lemon Shrimp

zest of 1 lemon	6 anchovy fillets, chopped
1/2 C. lemon juice	1 small red onion, thinly sliced
2 cloves garlic, crushed	1 bay leaf, crumbled
2 tbsp olive oil	pinch of cayenne powder
1 tbsp wine or sherry vinegar	1 to 1-1/2 lbs large shrimp
12 black olives	2 to 3 tsp salt

1. Pit and halve the black olives
2. Combine lemon zest, lemon juice, garlic, vinegar, oil, olives, anchovies, red onion, bay leaf, and cayenne; whisk well
3. Peel and clean shrimp, leaving tails on
4. Fill a pot half full with salted water and bring to a boil.
5. Add shrimp; boil for 1-1/2 to 2 minutes, until shrimp pinks and flesh looks opaque. Remove immediately.
6. Drain and set shrimp in marinade; if shrimp is not fully covered, add a bit of the shrimp poaching water
7. Cover and refrigerate 2 to 3 hours, turning shrimp once

Marie Rose Sauce

One of the things I learned only by going to Scotland was the prevalence of Marie Rose sauce, served with prawns. When I wrote a previous scene of Amy and Angus in a pub—the morning they had breakfast before setting out to England, when Amy meets Sinead—and her twin Siobhan—they were having breakfast. So it didn't really make sense for them to be having shrimp. For that scene, I had very clearly in mind a place I ate lunch in Killin, in which the owner's black and white collie happily wandered from guest to guest! (I think that dog found its way into that scene, too!) It was there I first had Rose Marie sauce.

Like any recipe, there are plenty of variations. Here's one:

1/4 C. mayonnaise	2 tsp horseradish
1 tbsp ketchup	1/4 tsp brandy
1 tbsp lemon juice	salt and pepper to taste
1 tbsp chives	1 lb large cooked shrimp

1. Mix all ingredients except shrimp
2. Add shrimp and toss, coating thoroughly with Marie Rose sauce

Simon Meets Amy at Melrose

Warmth settled around her, a relief from the cold wind outside. It had been a long walk. The ache was settling in her thighs, and she missed James. She watched curiously as the man across from her dug in his pocket and set a handful of bills on the table.

"Bring her what she wants," he told the waitress, without looking at the woman.

Once again, something in his vowels reminded her of Niall's speech. Niall had been a quick learner and an excellent mimic. But it had taken him time to copy the inflections and tones of the orchestra members' American speech. This man spoke with tones that were neither quite Scottish nor quite English.

"What'll you have, Love?" the waitress's pencil poised over a small pad.

Amy drew her attention from the man. "Coffee," she said. "With cream and sugar." She glanced at the pile of bills on the table. A twenty lay on top. It seemed a curious amount to put out for coffee. "And a cinnamon roll."

The waitress jotted on her pad and looked to the man.

"Coffee. And a cinnamon roll." He spoke with assurance and Amy thought she'd been hasty in hearing anything of Niall in his voice. He turned to her. "Simon Beaumont."

Cinnamon Rolls

1 C. warm water
1/2 C. heavy cream
4-1/2 tsp instant yeast
1 C. plus 2 tsp sugar
1/2 C. buttermilk,
   room temperature
2 tsp fine grain sea salt salt
2 large eggs, lightly whisked
⅓ C. canola oil
⅓ C. melted butter
7-8 C. all purpose flour
2 1/2" dots soy lecithin

Filling:
12 tbsp softened butter unsalted
2 C. 2 tbsp light brown sugar
1/2 C. white sugar
5 tbsp ground cinnamon
4 tbsp cornstarch
Frosting:
6 oz. cream cheese
   room temperature
4 tbsp unsalted butter, softened
1-1/2 tsp vanilla extract
1-1/2 tbsp corn syrup
2 to 2-1/2 C. powdered sugar

1. Stir water and cream together. Warm for 30 to 60 seconds in a microwave. It should not be hot
2. Add yeast and 2 tsp of sugar, set aside to foam for 5-10 minutes
3. In a separate bowl, heat the buttermilk only to lukewarm, then add to the water/cream/yeast
4. In another bowl, whisk together: remaining sugar, salt, oil, butter and eggs
5. Add this to the water/cream/yeast
6. Using a mixer, stir together with a dough hook
7. Add flour over the top and soy lecithin, and continue mixing until dough begins to form a ball
8. Mix another 3 minutes, adding an additional 1/4 cup flour if it seems to need more
9. Remove dough hook, cover the bowl with a towel, and set aside to rise, 1-2 hours in a warm place
10. On a lightly floured surface, roll dough into a large, even rectangle
11. Spread soft butter over dough, to the edges
12. Mix brown sugar, sugar, cinnamon, and corn starch
13. Sprinkle generously over the butter and dough, to the edges.
14. Roll dough into a tight log and slice it into your separate cinnamon buns. NOTE: a silpat does a better job of rolling dough into logs, and unflavored dental floss does a better job of slicing them. Slide floss under dough, bring it up and around, as if to tie it, then pull tight to slice through
15. Set buns out on a lightly greased baking sheet
16. Cover newly cut rolls with a towel and allow to rise 1 to 2 hours
17. Heat oven to 350 F; bake 20-22 minutes: as soon as they are golden, they are done!
18. *Frosting*: Whip cream cheese and butter with a hand mixer until soft. Add corn syrup and vanilla and mix further. Slowly beat in powdered sugar
19. Remove from oven, cool for 2 minutes
20. Frost while hot
21. Summon the serving wench to serve to a hapless young maiden....wait, no, that's Simon. Never mind that part!

Simon Dines with the Monks

The couple was gone! Simon watched their places as the handful of monks filed in for supper. They bowed tonsured heads over steepled fingers for prayer, clearly not expecting the seats to be filled. The blood began a low simmer in his veins as the soup that passed for a meal was placed before him, as his mind traveled back to the incident in the cemetery. The old man had lied to him. He'd deliberately led him deeper amongst the ruined stones, tempting him with gems of knowledge.

The simmer rose to a slow boil as he realized they had many hours head start, and would have many more; for he couldn't set out into the hills with night falling. He watched Eamonn, who never looked up from his soup. When the meal ended, the monks filed out on cat's feet, silent leather shoes brushing age-worn stone floors.

Preach not to others what they should eat, but eat as becomes you, and be silent.
~ Epictetus, 55-135 A.D.

Medieval Leek Soup

1/4 tsp coriander or cardamon
1 head of fresh cabbage
2 medium sized onions

2 whole leaks
3 C. water or chicken stock

1. Wash and chop cabbage and leeks; slice onions very thin
2. Put in a pot with water or stock
3. Boil, then lower heat and simmer for 15 minutes

Laura Vosika

The Medieval Monks' Mushroom Soup

Gnocchi the Modern

Did medieval Scottish monks think of it as gnocchi? Probably not, but they likely had plenty of methods of using flour, cheese, and eggs, and may well have made something *like* this, regardless of what they *called* it.

8 oz. ricotta cheese *	1 whole egg
1 oz. Finely grated Parmesan cheese	1 egg yolk
a pinch of salt	4 oz. all purpose flour

* 8 oz. *after* draining. Get ricotta cheese with *only* milk and salt, or possibly an acid or natural culture, in the ingredient list

1. Press ricotta between towels to drain (The monks would have used cloth towels. I will allow you to use paper towels, but be warned, it is not the medieval experience)
2. Mix cheese, eggs, flour, and salt with drained ricotta
3. On the ubiquitous lightly floured surface, pat dough into a rectangle (not a quadrilateral), and divide into four equal sections
4. Roll each section into a long thin log, divide each log in two and roll each of those into foot-long rolls (it's like monks with play-dough!), then cut logs into squares and dust with semolina flour
5. Drop squares into boiling water, stirring and boiling until they've been floating for about a minute

Or, from a medieval cookbook:

...take...fresh cheese and mash it, [take] flour and mix with egg yolks. Put a pot full of water on the fire and, when it begins to boil, put the mixture on a dish and drop it into the pot with a ladle. And when they are cooked, place them on dishes and sprinkle with plenty of grated cheese.

PREHEAT OVEN: 325 degrees F

1 lb mozzarella or farmer's cheese   4 eggs
2 C. flour

1. Grate cheese; crumble half of it into small pieces in a bowl
2. Add flour, mash well with cheese
3. Beat eggs, blend into flour/cheese, then knead well, until just a little bit sticky
4. Roll into small balls and drop into boiling, salted water
5. Boil until they rise to the top, then remove
6. Put in a baking dish, sprinkle with grated cheese
7. Bake just long enough to melt cheese on top

And now, the soup:

9 oz. chanterelle mushrooms	1 tsp marjoram
9 oz. crimini mushrooms	4 tbsp oil
18 oz. dried porcini mushrooms	1 leek
3/4 C. sherry	2 garlic cloves, crushed
4 C. water	1 C. port wine
8 sprigs thyme	salt and pepper
4-5 C. fresh gnocchi	parsley
2 oz. butter	

1. Soak porcini mushrooms in sherry for 1 hour.
2. Put the other mushrooms, cleaned, in a pot with water, a dash of sherry, marjoram, and thyme
3. Cook mushrooms until softened; remove, saving water, and slice
4. Saute diced onion in butter and oil
5. Drain porcini mushrooms, save sherry, squeeze out fluid and slice
6. Mix all mushrooms together, add to onions; simmer 15 minutes
7. Add garlic, sherry, and port wine to pan and simmer 5 minutes
8. Add thyme sprigs from saved water, salt and pepper, and simmer
9. Put gnocchi into bowls and spoon mushroom soup on top
10. Garnish with parsley

Niall and Hugh arrive at Ayr for Parliament

Niall, Hugh and their thirty men flowed, with ever-growing numbers of others, over hillocks into the town of Ayr. They arrived barely on time, hampered by steady rain and hills treacherous with thick mud. Douglas arrived from his nearby lands. Great lords filed in from north, east, and south, giving Ayr the feel of a fair day, with peddlers selling food and ale to the gathering army, children darting and shouting among the newcomers, horses snorting and nickering, and the smells of sweat and damp wool and horseflesh filling every street.

Niall felt, still, the sting of being passed over for the Isle of Man. Here, in Ayr, war plans would be laid. As much as he wanted to be back with Allene, he needed to be here, ready to fight for his king—to redeem his failure.

Spiced Nuts

PREHEAT OVEN: 350 degrees

1 lb nuts, whole or chopped	1 C. sugar
1-1/2 sticks unsalted butter	1 tsp cinnamon
2 egg whites, beaten	

1. Salt nuts lightly; bake on a baking sheet 8 minutes and cool
2. Whip egg whites into a meringue, blend in melted butter, sugar and cinnamon
3. Fold all ingredients together and lay out on a baking sheet
4. Bake 30 minutes, stirring every 10 minutes

Compost (Fruits and Vegetables Pickled in Honey and Wine)

Take rote of persel, of pasternak, of rafens, scrape hem and waische hem
clene. Take rapes & caboches, ypared and icorue. Take an erthen panne
with clene water & set it on the fire; cast alle þise perinne. Whan þey
buth boiled cast þerto peeres, & parboile hem wel. Take alle þise
thynges vp & lat it kele on a faire cloth. Do þerto salt; whan it is colde,
do hit in a vessel; take vyneger & powdour & safroun & do þerto, & lat
alle þise thynges lye þerin al nyyt, oþer al day. Take wyne greke & hony,
clarified togider; take lumbarde mustard & raisons coraunce, al hoole,
& grynde powdour of canel, powdour douce & aneys hole, & fenell
seed. Take alle þise thynges & cast togyder in a pot of erthe, & take
þerof whan þou wilt & serue forth.
~ 14th century *Forme of Cury*

parsley	3 C. red wine
1 lb carrots	1/2 C. honey
1/2 lb radishes	1/2 tsp lumbard mustard
1/2 head cabbage	whole currants
3/4 C. currants	1/2 tsp cinnamon
2 tsp salt	1/2 tsp powder douce
6 tbsp white or white wine vinegar	1 tsp anise seed
1/4 tsp powder (fine)	1 tsp fennel seed
1/2 tsp saffron	

1. Clean, peel, pare, and core all vegetables as needed
2. Bring vegetables to a boil in a pot of water
3. When they've boiled, add pears and boil well
4. Remove vegetables from water and let them cool
5. Add salt
6. When cooled, place in a large bowl; add vinegar, powder douce, mustard, and saffron, and let sit overnight
7. Mix in currants and seeds
8. Mix together honey, wine, and cinnamon, and bring to a boil, removing 'scum' that rises to the top
9. Pour over fruits and vegetables

Amy and Angus After Visiting Eamonn in the Hospital

Angus's kitchen feels like warmth and home. Chicken bubbles in the crockpot, reminding me of happy times with him. I wonder, did he plan on us living here? Or buying a house together? I'd have been happy with either. I wanted only to be with him. His steadfastness. His humor. His quick smile. The dark shadow on his jaw in the evening. But time traveling ghosts and my traitorous emotions have slammed a minor chord to the end of our short symphony.

Angus swings the crockpot to the table, and slides a ladle in it. In his car seat, James lets out a short squeal. Angus's face softens. He stoops, and lifts him, crooning. James's face lights up.

I spoon chicken, in creamy white sauce, onto my plate. "Am I being paranoid? About Simon?"

"Better paranoid than sorry."

I poke my fork at my chicken.

He reaches across the small table for my hand. "I'm sorry." *His words are husky.*

"I'm sorry, too. I didn't...." *I stop. I can't pretend Shawn didn't affect me. No words are adequate. I know in my heart I want to be with Angus, but I also know how I'd feel if I saw him so emotional over Julia. I clear my throat.* "Brother Eamonn promised me James is safe."

"We don't know how lucid he is," *Angus reminds me.*

I have no answer. I push at the chicken.

"You read the prophecy?"

"I wrestled with it." *I force down a bite of chicken, untasted. I raise my eyes.* "Just reading it doesn't hurt him."

He strokes James's cheek. "I can't endanger him."

I stare at chives floating in Alfredo sauce. "He seemed lucid. How do I balance all these competing needs? James, you, Shawn, Carol?"

Angus lifts his eyes. "If you quit for me, you'd hold it against me one day" *He looks down at James in his arms.* "So might he."

"But I hurt you by continuing. I might endanger James. I don't even know if it's possible to bring him back. If I called it off...?"

"I want what we had." *He touches my hand.* "But right now, we don't."

"Choosing you, for the rest of my life means nothing?" *Anger flashes through me. But at least we're acknowledging it now.* "If you disappeared, I'd be just as upset."

He stares at his untouched food. "You must do what gives you peace."

Chicken in White Wine

2 tbsp butter, melted
4 boneless, skinless chicken breasts
1 tsp salt
1/4 tsp pepper
4 garlic cloves, finely chopped
1-1/2 lbs baby portabella mushrooms

12 oz. frozen white pearl onions
1/2 C. dry white wine
1 tsp dried thyme leaves
1 bay leaf
1 C. chicken broth
1/3 C. flour

1. Slice chicken breasts in half and slice mushrooms into thick slices
2. Put butter, chicken, salt, pepper, garlic, mushrooms, onions, wine, thyme, and bay leaf into a crock pot
3. Combine chicken broth and flour, whisk well, pour into crock pot and stir
4. Cover, set to low, and cook 5-6 hours
5. Remove and discard bay leaf, unless you have a really good use for bay leaves

Explaining Blessed Knife

"They're very ascetic." She jumped back into the topic. "Small and private, even today. They copy manuscripts by hand, pray, and farm everything they need. They're strict vegetarians, probably as a result of the blessed knife."

"Which was what?" Amy asked.

"Columba blessed a knife, somewhat absent-mindedly, while he wrote." Helen's piercing clicked on her teeth as she spoke, drawing Amy's attention with its rhythm. "Only later did he ask if it would harm man or beast. When the monks said it was for slaughtering animals, he put a blessing on it, that it would never harm men or cattle. They found the poor butcher boy outside, struggling with all his might to kill a cow for the monks' dinner. Columba's blessing prevented him doing so. "So they melted it down and used the metal to coat farm tools, so no one would be harmed by them. And believe it or not, this relates to the crucifix."

History

The story of Columba and the blessed knife is a true one. Or, it is a well-known story, at the very least. Luckily, vegetables were plentiful in medieval times. We've already seen some of them. Here are a few recipes the Monks might have known—and Shawn likely would *not* have loved!

Sprouts

There are five types of cabbage: the best are those which have witnessed the first frost and are tender and ready to be cooked. In the cold temperatures it is not suitable to parboil them but in rainy weather it is. (And start each so that each year they begin growing in April, and then end near the harvest, Christmas, and Easter)

White cabbage comes in towards the end of August.

Cabbage heads grow near the end of harvest. And when the cabbage head, which is in the middle, is picked, the stem of the cabbage is taken and replanted in new earth, and large leaves will grow and spread and the cabbage will use a lot of space. And these cabbages are given the name of Roman cabbage, and they are eaten in winter. And the stems can be replanted, growing little cabbages which are called cabbage sprouts, that can be eaten with fresh herbs in vinegar. And when in abundance, they are well-enjoyed washed in warm water, and in their entirety cooked in a little bit of water, and when they are cooked, put on them salt and oil, and serve a large amount without water, and put olive oil on top during Lent.

~ Le Menagier de Paris

1 lb Brussels sprouts	3 tbsp marjoram
1/2 C. white wine vinegar	1/2 tsp dried tarragon
2 tbsp olive oil	1 tbsp parsley
1/4 C. chopped onion	1 tsp salt
1 clove garlic, minced	pepper
2 tbsp honey	

1. Put all ingredients in a pan, heat to boiling
2. Simmer, covered, until tender

Vegetable soup

1 oz. unsalted butter	1/2 lb mushrooms, sliced
1 large carrot	1 onion, sliced
2 stalks celery	1/2 tsp ground turmeric
1/4 lb rutabagas, sliced thin	32 fl. oz. vegetable stock
1/2 lb turnips	chives, snipped to garnish

1. Slice carrot and celery into matchsticks (but do not light them!)
2. Saute vegetables in melted butter 5 minutes, stirring occasionally
3. Add turmeric and cook for another minute
4. Add stock, bring to a boil, and simmer for 20 minutes
5. Garnish with chives

Bringing Food to Bruce and Angus Og

Niall entered the tavern, head bowed, and found the basket and jug stashed behind the counter.

"That yours?" the innkeeper asked. Niall gave a silent nod, collecting it, and carried it, monk-like, to the Bruce's room.

"The not-so-silent Brother Andrew!" Angus Og's voice burst through the doorway. "We'd thought to go looking for our dinner."

Niall bowed silently, and set the food on the table, his head low.

"We've a mission for you, Brother Andrew." Bruce reached for a hunk of cheese. "You know where to find Jamie Douglas?"

Niall nodded. His heart picked up a quick beat. James Douglas was speeding through Jedburgh forest on his way to another series of lightning strikes against the English. With a fast horse, he could find him and be back on time to sail.

Bruce sliced off a piece of cheese with his dirk. "I'm given to understand you're more than willing to break your vow of silence when necessary."

Niall kept quiet, though he fumed at Shawn's callous disregard for the gravity of a monkish vow. He gave a nod—a silent nod.

In the narrow field of vision left by the hood, Bruce's hand tapped a scroll on the desk, then pushed it toward him. "Deliver this to Sir James. The English are heading north to meet him. He must be warned. Understand?"

Niall nodded, accepting the scroll.

"Make haste, good brother. God go with you."

Hildegard

Hildegard of Bingen advised, "If one wishes to eat cheese, it should be neither cooked nor fresh, but dried...." Of one of her many visions, she says, "....I also saw the earth with people on it. The people were carrying milk in their vessels, and they were making cheese from the milk. Some of the milk was thick, from which strong cheese was being made; some of the milk was thin, from which mild cheese was being curdled; and some of the milk was spoiling, from which bitter cheese was being produced."

On The Recipes Chosen

Although nobility would typically eat finer food, Bruce, in this scene, is in a temporary headquarters in Ayr, preparing to launch a naval attack. Bruce was a man of deep faith, and one used to living hard if that's what his country needed. All I know of his character tells me he would be living and working alongside his men, more focused on the problem at hand than on dining like a king. The town of Ayr would have had a huge influx, with Bruce's and Angus Og's men descending on it, and preparing to launch a naval fleet, which must be victualed for the journey. The town merchants would certainly have scrambled to feed so many visitors.

Therefore, I think it's quite plausible his cheese would have been something on the simpler side.

Queso Blanco

1 gal pasteurized whole milk   1/4 C. vinegar (apple cider)

1. In a large stainless steel pot, directly heat the milk to between 185° and 190°F, stirring often
2. When it is steamy and foamy, slowly add vinegar, until the curds separate from the whey
3. Pour curds and whey into a colander line with butter muslin or a light towel
4. Tie corners of muslin into a knot and hang to drain for 2 to 3 hours
5. Voila! Serve to the king! Or eat it yourself. No, on second thought, it's much safer to serve it to the king who is waiting!

NOTE: Acids can be substituted: vinegar for savory, lemon or lime juice for a dessert cheese

Soft Cheese

1 gal whole pasteurized milk   2 tsp kosher salt
1 pt heavy pasteurized cream   2 tbsp powdered ginger
1/4 C. apple cider vinegar   2 tbsp honey

1. Heat milk and cream in a large non-reactive pot: this means ceramic, enamel (not scratches or chips), glass, plastic (which is not available to my medieval readers, so do not use it!) or stainless steel
2. Stir frequently until it reaches 190 °F, then turn off heat
3. Add vinegar slowly, stirring only the top inch of the mixture. Use only as much vinegar as it takes to form curds well
4. When precipitation begins, let sit for 5 minutes
5. Pour curds and whey into a colander lined with muslin
6. Tie corners of muslin together and hang for 2-3 hours, to drain
7. Put muslin bag with cheese in it in a colander set in a pot; put a small plate on top of bag and set a 3 to 4 pound weight on plate
8. Refrigerate: After 12 or more hours, put cheese in large bowl with salt, ginger and honey and mix well with hands
9. Eat (which, when it comes to cheese, I *highly* recommend, and definitely with olives and wine) or, if there is a king waiting for his dinner, serve it to him!

Herb Bread

Van coeck te backen
Neemt tarwenmeel oft bloemen met warmen watere also vele als ghi
behoeft, ende wercket een luttel samen, dan neemt venckelsaet ende spec
ghesneden terlincxwijse ende doeget int deech ende wercket wel tsamen
tot tay deech ende maect eenen ronden coec ende bacten in den oven
metten brode oft op den heert, &c. Inde plaetse vanden spec moech dy
nemen boter oft olijfoly. Men bact ooc coec onder de asschencolen, mer
sonder spec, met sout, venckel ende olie.

PREHEAT OVEN: 375 degrees F

2 packages yeast	6 tbsp oil
2 C. hot water	1-1/2 tsp rosemary
7 large eggs	2/3 C. parsley
1-1/4 tsp salt	8 C. flour

1. Dissolve yeast in water
2. Combine 6 eggs, salt, oil, herbs and 3 cups of flour
3. Add yeast and mix well
4. Add more flour to a dough consistency and knead on floured board for 10 minutes
5. Place in greased bowl; cover and allow to rise for 1-1/2 hours in a warm place
6. Shape into two loaves and set on baking sheet
7. Cover loosely and allow to rise for another 45 minutes
8. Beat last egg and brush loaf with it
9. Bake for 50 minutes

Shawn Returns from Jura

"Brother Andrew returned but hours after ye left," the daughter of the house informed Shawn, when he arrived back in Ayr. "He's been quiet this past week, Milord."

"About time." Shawn swung his cloak off, shaking rainwater from it. The thought of a warm, dry bed was heaven. "He's had a wee problem with his vow of silence." He grinned. "Got something to break our fast?" His father would have had fun talking like that.

The girl dimpled and blushed. All sorts of good feelings rushed Shawn's head. But as he headed down the narrow hall to the back room, clutching a basket of bread and cheese in one arm, he twisted Christina's kerchief into a tight cord between nervous fingers. He forced himself to unwrap it and tuck it back in his sleeve, staring at the scarred wooden door. Niall would be mad. In fact, mad wouldn't begin to describe what Niall would be.

History

In *Westering Home,* Shawn explains Jura succinctly to Amy:

> Shawn headed down a narrow road to the beach, and she fell into step beside him. "The battle of Jura. Weird to give it a name. To us, it just was. John of Lorn was being difficult, playing admiral of the high seas for Edward in England. Except they were our high seas. So we paid him a visit."
>
> "On the high seas?" Amy raised her eyebrows.

One of the lesser known but more interesting stories from the time of Robert the Bruce is the sea battle against Sir John of Lorne– more colorfully known as Lame John of Lorne or Ian Bacach. Or, because it's good to have plenty of names to choose from, John MacDougall.

Yes, *those* MacDougalls. Lame John was the son of Alexander MacDougall. Though this Alexander, uncle to John Comyn who was murdered by Bruce, died a few years before Bannockburn, Nigel Tranter places *an* Alexander MacDougall at the August 1314 council, as one of many who sided with the English but quickly came back into the peace of Robert the Bruce afterward.

On the part of Bruce, his famed mercy was not merely mercy for the sake of mercy, but the hope of a practical man who believed his country would be stronger—and better and safer for all—if he could bring his people together, rather than having them fight against one another. To this end, he offered mercy for the price of allegiance.

Lame John did not accept this offer of peace, but continued to serve Edward II of England, as admiral in the western Isles. Having decreed that Scotland must stand united, Bruce did not care overly much for Edward II's ships in his Sound of Jura. Dates are uncertain: some sources indicate June 1315, a year to the day after Bannockburn, while others suggest 1316 or even 1317.

Regardless of the year, it's a fascinating battle and a fascinating look at Bruce, who once again showed his ingenuity and ability to use everything he had—even history and superstition.

This is one of many battles in which the colorful Angus Og, Lord of the Isles, worked side by side with Bruce, as one of his most loyal supporters. His fleet transported his own Islemen and Bruce's warriors. Half the ships, under Angus Og, sailed around and up the western shore of Kintyre, into the southern Sound of Jura where Lame John's fleet lay. At the same time, Bruce's men sailed up the eastern shore of the peninsula—into East Loch Tarbert, which has no outlet—unless, of course, you're the Bruce. (Or perhaps Chuck Norris. But Chuck Norris wasn't alive then. I think the Bruce was the Chuck Norris of his day.)

Bruce had his men build a 'path' of logs. They then hauled the galleys, with ropes, up onto the rollers, and between pulling and opening the sails, Bruce 'sailed' a mile overland, into West Loch Tarbert. From there, presumably with men exhausted from days of rowing, chopping, and hauling ships, Bruce sailed into the north of the Sound of Jura.

The genius of Bruce's plan, apart from the element of surprise—for there was no waterway to allow ships to surprise John from the north, so he could not possibly have expected that!—was that it played on an old superstition, that arose in 1098 when Magnus Barefoot, King of Norway, did the same thing.

In the words of John Barbour, medieval author of *The Brus*: "For they knew by an old prophecy that whoever should have ships go between those seas with sails would so win the Isles for himself that no one could withstand him by force. Therefore, they all came to the King and none withstood his commands apart from John of Lorn alone." Of course, he said it in medieval Englys. I'm guessing it also boosted the morale of Bruce's men, who must have been exhausted by this point.

Lame John's fleet was now caught between Angus Og coming up from the south and Bruce coming down from the north. Between the clear military problem and the superstitions of his men, John of Lorn had little chance. Nigel Tranter paints a colorful picture of the event, describing it as taking place in the hours near dark at Midsummer's Night, with torches lighting up close to the water, along the lines of

Bruce's and Angus Og's galleys to signal one another, and John driving his fleet hard to the west, trying futilely to escape the trap.

The battle of Jura ended swiftly, the isles completely under the power of Robert Bruce and Angus Og, and John of Lorn not to live many months beyond that event.

And on the return of his men, Shawn brings cheese and bread to Niall, who he made sure was left behind.

Farmstead Cheese

1 gallon of milk   2 tsp very fine sea salt
1/2 C. white vinegar

1. Bring milk to a boil over medium heat, stirring frequently
2. When it boils, immediately turn heat to low; stir in vinegar
3. If milk does not immediately separate into curds and whey, add vinegar, a tbsp at a time, until it does
4. Pour curds and whey into a colander lined with butter muslin
5. Rinse with cool water and sprinkle with salt
6. Tie up cheesecloth
7. Squeeze to remove excess whey, then hang for 1 to 2 hours

Barley & Rye Bread

PREHEAT OVEN: 400 degrees F

2 C. coarse barley meal   1 C. barm
1 C. cracked wheat   2 C. warm water
4 - 6 C. dark rye flour

1. Soak barley and cracked wheat in 2 cups warm water
2. Drain barley and cracked wheat and add to rye flour
3. Add barm; stir until too stiff to work
4. On floured surface, knead until smooth and elastic
5. Cover, set aside to rise until double in size, about two hours
6. Punch down, shape into loaf, cover and let rise another hour
7. Bake about one hour

With Christina MacRuari

Niall's company rested at Castle Tioram with Christina MacRuari. Pleasant as Shawn found it, playing Niall that evening, listening to stories in the great hall, watching jugglers and acrobats, playing harp—pleasant as it was wandering the gardens that night—it was still life on the road, with no one, not Amy, not Christina, to make it home.

He longed for his bed at Glenmirril, as he roamed Tioram's rain-dampened courtyard, robed as Brother Andrew. He remembered clearly what it would look like in seven hundred years, broken down and lonely on its wind-swept coast. He remembered every detail of the night he would spend here with Amy, exactly where he would sing to her by the picnic basket. The stars would dance overhead on a clear night just as they did tonight. He remembered painfully, the text message to the writer in New York. Debra? Jo? It soured his heart, knowing he'd hurt Amy, broken her trust and love, for a woman whose name he couldn't even remember.

He touched the gray stones of the courtyard wall. Fresh ivy clung to it, drops of rain shining like diamonds on each leaf, not the dead vines that would shroud dry crumbled walls centuries from now. Laughter drifted from the sparkling new great hall, ladies and knights laughing at the jester's antics.

The smell of roasting venison drifted out. Amy felt like a dream slipping from his grasp. His son, James, felt like a whisper on the wind, a rumor he could only hope was true

Bear in mind that you should conduct yourself in life as at a feast.
~ Epictetus, 55-135 A.D.

Venison Poached in Red Wine

2 lbs venison steaks	1 tsp cinnamon
4 pieces of bacon	1 tsp ginger
2 C. red wine	pinch saffron, ground
1 C. water	

1. Chop venison and bacon into small pieces
2. Put into a large pot with all other ingredients
3. Bring to a boil, then simmer for about 20 minutes.

Gourdes in Potage

Gourdes in Potage. Take young Gowrdes; pare hem and kerue hem on pecys. Cast hem in gode broth, and do þerto a gode pertye of oynouns mynced. Take pork soden; grynde it and alye it þerwith and wiþ yolkes of ayren. Do þerto safroun and salt, and messe it forth with powdour douce.

~ 14th century, *Forme of Cury*

Makerouns (noodles and cheese)

Makerouns. Take and make a thynne foyle of dowh, and kerue it on pieces, and cast hym on boiling water & seeþ it wele. Take chese and grate it, and butter imelte, cast bynethen and abouven as losyns; and serue forth.

~*Forme of Cury*, 14th century

Beef Red Wine Stew

Beef stewed in red wine is well known today. It dates back many centuries.

1/2 C. ground almonds	1/4 tsp ground cloves
1/2 tsp clear honey	3 tsp sugar
1 C. hot water	1/4 tsp ground cloves
2 lbs stewing beef	1/2 tsp pepper
1/2 C. breadcrumbs	1/2 tsp allspice
1/4 C. butter	1 tsp ground mace
1 C. red wine	1 tsp salt

1. Dissolve honey in hot water.
2. Pour into a bowl with ground almonds
3. Steep 15 to 30 minutes; strain out almonds
4. Cut beef into chunks and roll them in breadcrumbs
5. Fry in butter, turning until meat is browned.
6. Move to a large cooking pot.
7. In a separate pan add wine, cloves and sugar and stir over medium heat until sugar dissolves
8. Pour this over the meat, cover with a lid and simmer 40 minutes. Do not let it dry out!
9. Stir in remaining spices and almond milk
10. Heat and serve.

Raiding with James Douglas

Other days, Shawn covered his hair with a coif, shielded his face in Brother Andrew's hood, and spent hours felling trees in the drizzle, and crafting them into the belfries and sows with which Bruce would assault Carlisle. On those days, Niall sacked Hartlepool with Douglas. By night, one or the other of them played harp by the campfire, while men thrust chunks of English beef, sizzling, and dripping juices, over the flames. Rain dripped off the trees above as they sang of ancient victories and heroes. The harmonies of the harp reverberated in Shawn's fingers and through his body, healing him from the exertions and bloodshed and screams of the wounded that each day brought.

When the Kye Come Hame, traditional

Come, all ye jolly shepherds
That whistle through the glen
I'll tell ye o' a secret that courtiers dinna ken
What is the greatest bliss that the tongue o' man can name?
'Tis to woo a bonnie lassie, when the kye come ham
When the kye come hame, when the kye come hame
Tween the gloamin' and the mirk
When the kye come hame.
'Tis not beneath the burgonet
Nor yet beneath the crown
'Tis not on couch of velvet
Nor yet on bed of down
'Tis beneath the spreading birch
In the dell without a name
Wi' a bonnie, bonnie lassie
When the kye come hame.
Awa' wi' fame and fortune
What comforts can they gi'e?
And a' the arts that prey upon
Man's life and liberty!
Gi'e me the highest joy
That the heart o' man can frame
My bonnie, bonnie lassie
When the kye come hame

kye cattle   *mirk* dark, night

And the cattle were....

Not quite like our cattle today. Today's livestock has gone through a great deal of breeding, to bring out certain traits—in particular, size, to give more meat at market. Medieval cattle were significantly smaller.

Our best source for knowing what they looked like is the famous Chillingham Cattle. This herd has remained untouched by human breeding or interference for 800 years—well before Niall's time. They live near Chillingham Castle in northern England, penned into many acres, but otherwise left to live as wild cattle did 800 years ago.

A bull in the Chillingham herd today weighs about 880 pounds, while the average bull today weighs from 2000 to 3300 pounds. The females weight about 620 pounds, as compared to today's full-grown Holsteins, which weight 1500, and can get up to 1800 pounds.

Beef

To powder befe with in a ny3t
Þou welle þo salt, in water bry3t;
Malt hit in bryne, set doun to kele,
Put in þy flesshe fayre and wele,
And in a ny3t hit poudert schalle be,
Grene powdert þorogh, so mot I þe.
Yf þy dysshe metes dere ben to salt,
kerve a grene sod, I wot, þou schalt,
And kover þy pot with þo gresse done,
Þo salt on þo gresse shalle barke fulle sone.
With þy honde smyte of, I say;
Þo salt lay on anew þou may;
Þys schalt þou gedur hit, yche a dele,
And make hit fresshe unto þe mele.
If I schalle of þese potage spelle
A whyle þeron þen most I dwelle;
Fyrste, to speke of furmenté,
How hit is made in yche degre
~ Liber Cure Cocorum

To build a Campfire

1. Find wood. In damp weather, look inside upright, dead trees for dry wood. If you have only a knife and must chop wood, place the blade against the log in need of cutting and hit the back of the knife with a chunk of wood about a foot long. Do this in the same V shape you would chop with an axe.
2. You can get dry wood from inside a log. To do so, set the log upright and place the log across it. Press the handle down hard and strike the tip with the same foot-long piece of wood.
3. Chop or cut down wood into thin, finger and wrist-sized pieces for kindling.
4. Set up a log or limb of a few inches length as a backstop and a place to build the fire.
5. Use very fine, dry bark shavings as tinder. Scrape your flint hard against your knife. In modern terms, draw a ferro rod sharply backwards against the blade of the knife. It will shoot sparks that will catch the tinder.
6. Add wood slowly, starting with the smallest pieces of kindling. Let the flame hit their narrowest sides. Continue with the smallest sizes until there's a decent blaze going. Blowing into the fire can help. Make it a slow, steady breath.

Cocking Beef over the Fire

Given a choice, build your fire with hardwoods—maple, oak, cherry, apple, peach are some good ones. Elder can be. If you must use willow, remove the bark. If you must use soft woods, grill over coals only, as the soft woods' smoke affects the taste of the food.

For a thick slab of meat, sear 3 to 4 minutes per side for a medium rare result. If you'd like your meat medium, try another 3 to 4 minutes per side.

Siege of Berwick

The cold woke Shawn long before his shift on guard duty. He sat up inside the pitch black he shared with Hugh. He tugged his tartan close, gathered his bag of oats, and crawled out into the starry night. Embers glowed in the fire pit. He stirred it up, adding kindling. An occasional flake of snow drifted down and sizzled in the heat while he fixed bannocks over the small flames. It was at least warmer than fording mountain passes had been, heading to Jedburgh with Hugh, Brother David, and three dozen of Niall's men.

January had blown in with cold winds and flurries in Douglas's wooded glens and rugged hills. On the fourteenth, they attacked Berwick by land and sea, zeroing in on an unfinished section of the town wall. But moon glow, as bright as a helicopter spotlight, slapped an abrupt coda on the attempt, like a pair of cymbals crashing to the floor. Berwick's garrison poured into the gap in the wall.

"Tell me more of your time," Hugh said, as they settled on a dark ridge overlooking the camp's eastern flank.

"For starters," Shawn said, "if I were there now, I'd be planning a big surprise for Amy for Valentine's Day."

"What's that?" Hugh chewed the hard bannock.

"A day for love. You never heard of St. Valentine? I'd think in this holy time, you'd know your saints."

Hugh chuckled. "It might be Malcolm knows of him."

"Aw, hell," Shawn said, "maybe he hasn't even been born, yet. Or maybe when Niall and I changed history, it killed off his ancestors and he never will be. I don't even know where he was from."

At the sight of Dumbarton once again,
We'll cock up our bannets and march amain;
Wi' braid claymores hangin' doun to our heel
To whang at the bannocks o' barley-meal."

~John, Duke of Argyll

History

In the years before his death in 1307, Edward I had taken many of Scotland's castles. He 1296, his army sacked Berwick, killing most of its citizens, including—stories say—a woman in the very act of childbirth. After 1307, Bruce steadily regained Scotland's lands and castle, with Berwick being the last holdout. The Scots made several failed attempts to take it, before succeeding in 1317. Before this, however, there was a long siege of the city, during which Douglas's Valentine's Day fight at Skaithmuir, against the Gascons, occurred. He would later say it was the hardest battle he had ever fought.

From September 1317 until that November, the Scots returned, still in vain, to their siege. It must have been a dull time, waiting and watching, with little to do other than make sure no one left Berwick. In April 1318, one Peter Spaulding reached out to the Scots (to use our modern terminology), offering to let them into the city. Although English himself, his wife was Scottish, and was being harassed—and I tend to think, given Peter's actions, possibly worse—by the English.

Let this be a lesson: Your city may survive military might, but fall to the bad behavior of your own soldiers. Not that that has anything to do with bannocks. But it's still pretty important.

Bannocks

The 'girdle' was a primary part of the Scots' cooking equipment—for pancakes, oatcakes, crumpets, potatoes, and oatmeal scones—and on the campaign trail, perhaps the only cooking equipment. Even bread was baked on the girdle rather than in the oven. These breads—or bannocks—were unleavened, about the size of a dinner plate, made from barley flour or oatmeal. In later years, bannocks came to be made with wheat flour, yeast, butter, and dried fruit. Today, the name bannock means any baked item similar in size and shape to the original bannock.

Scotland's staple cereal crops were barley and oats. Wheat didn't grow well in Scotland, and so our ever-present wheat flour was...not so ever-present to them. So, for the nearest experience to what the Scots ate as they besieged Berwick, use barley or oats. I would strongly advise against camping out around Berwick's city walls with a trebuchet while you do so, however. There's such a thing as getting too authentic. That's when the authorities get called.

As with virtually any recipe, there are many ways to skin a....no, I think that's a poor choice of expression in a cookbook. There are multiple ways of making any particular meal.

The Basic Bannock

barley or oatmeal   a very little bit of water

1. Mix oats or barley with a little water until firm
2. Shape into a flat cake and fry it on your girdle*

*Your medieval Scottish girdle, not your mother's girdle. This would most likely upset your mother. And possibly set fire to her girdle, thus resulting in you going into battle hungry. Really—use the right girdle!

This actually works, and is fairly tasty! Add salt for a little more flavor—you will have to decide if your particular medieval regiment happens to have salt on hand. The fun of cooking is that you can take any basic recipe and do as you like with it. I decided my medieval Scots just might have access to parsley and fennel during a siege, as many medieval recipes use these two ingredients.

The Medieval Besieger's Gourmet Oatcake

barley or oatmeal   fennel
a little water   parsley
salt

1. Mix oats or barley with a little water
2. Sprinkle in parsley and fennel. The medieval Scots besieging Berwick did not have measuring spoons, so just sprinkle some in
3. Shape it into a flat cake and fry it on your girdle. See * above.

And of course, there's no reason you can't mash up and mix in any berries you find growing in the area. Since this particular siege happened in the fall and early spring, I'm not sure that will be much. But if you happen to be at a summertime siege, or be a modern reader, this could work very well.

Also—of course—add any herbs or spices you like.

Bainne Bannock

Bainne (BAHN-yuh) is Gaelic for milk, and *bainne bannock* just sounds so much cooler than milk oatcake.

barley meal	salt
butter	sweet milk

1. Put a cup of milk, salt, and an ounce or so of butter in a pan
2. Bring to a boil, then—swift as the fleeing English army at Bannockburn—stir in enough barley/oatmeal) to make dough
3. Bake in rounds over a hot fire—or on your stove top if you prefer

Hare Boiled in a Pot

The mountain hare, known by a number of other names (blue hare, tundra hare, variable hare, Irish hare, snow hare, and alpine hare, is the only hare native to Scotland. The European rab/bit was brought by the Romans. It did not become widespread in Scotland until the 1800s, but maybe that's because the besiegers and soldiers kept eating them! It seems almost certain that a besieging army would have made good use of the hare in the forest. A medieval source tells us:

Take hares and flay them; pick the bones clean; hew them into pieces and put them into a pot with the blood, and seeth them. Then put them into cold water. Put the broth with other good stock, almond milk, and parboiled minced onions. Let it boil on the fire. Add powder of cloves, cinnamon, and mace, and a little vinegar. Take the well-washed flesh, and the bones, and set them all to boil in the broth, and then serve.

hare	minced onions
ground cloves	almond milk
cinnamon	a little vinegar
mace	

1. Put hare meat and blood into a pot and bring to a boil
2. Put meat into cold water and let sit
3. To the broth, add almond milk and onions; bring to a boil
4. Add spices, vinegar, meat and bones, and boil again

Be aware, when it comes to this hare, I haven't tried it—I didn't dare. This is merely a report of what this recipe is saying there.

Hares in onion sauce

The *Liber Cure Cocorum* gives us more ways—in rhyme—to prepare hare (an unavoidable rhyme)

Harus in cyne.

Perboyle þe hare and larde hit wele,
Sethyn loke þou rost hir everydele;
Take onyons and loke þou hew hom smalle,
Frye hom in grece, take peper and ale,
And grynde togeder þo onyons also;
Coloure hit with safrone and welle hit þo;
Lay þe hare in charioure, as I þe kenne;
Powre on þe sewe and serve hit þenne.
~ *Liber Cure Cocorum*

Hares in a stew

Harus in a sewe.

Alle rawe þo hare schalle hacked be,
In gobettis smalle, Syr, levys me;
In hir owne blode seyn or sylud clene,
Grynde brede and peper withalle bydene;
Þenne temper hit with þe same bre,
Þenne boyled and salted hit servyd schalle be.
~ *Liber Cure Cocorum*

Boiled Hare

1 rabbit	1 oz. flour
4 oz. bacon, diced	1/4 pt milk
1 large onion, chopped	1 tbsp chopped parsley
salt and pepper	a little vinegar
1 pt water	

1. Soak rabbit in cold water and vinegar, about two hours
2. Drain; slice and dice rabbit meat
3. Put rabbit meat, bacon, onion, salt, pepper, and water into a pot
4. Cook over low to medium heat, 1-1/2 hours, until rabbit is tender
5. In a bowl, dissolve flour in milk, then stir into rabbit stew
6. Bring to a boil, stirring until it thickens and becomes smooth
7. Season to taste and garnish with parsley

As with any recipe, feel free to change up the seasonings. Or add some vegetables. Or stew in red wine. This is the fun of cooking!

Fruit Tart

There are few enough cookbooks left to us from medieval times, but none that I've found that record recipes of medieval armies on the march —let alone medieval armies on the march, living off the land. I did, however, find a journal that talks about a large group of men living off the land—a very similar situation to that of the medieval Scottish army —and that is Lewis and Clark, who recorded their journey across 3,700 miles of wilderness, living largely off the land. And, as relates to food, this is what makes their journal fascinating: they did not live merely off game and wild berries, as I might have imagined. They have left us a record of fruit tarts.

I figure if a corps of men thousands of miles from the nearest town can have fruit tarts, so can the medieval Scottish army, camped outside Berwick. Although they may have been living largely in tents or outdoors, they would have had access to other towns, from which they might have bought flour and sugar. So, my medieval army gets fruit tarts on a special occasion, although they may well prefer whisky. Too bad. Tonight, they get fruit tarts. Tomorrow, whisky.

Fruit Tart

PREHEAT OVEN/CAMPFIRE: 375 degrees F

Pastry:
1 C. all-purpose flour
1/4 C. whole wheat flour
4 tbsp butter
2 to 3 tbsp cold water
1/4 C. lard or shortening

Filling:
2 lbs fresh fruit
1/3 C. all purpose flour
1/3 to 1/2 C. of sugar

Pastry:
1. Combine flours and salt, then cut in lard and 3 tbsp of butter until the dough is in pea-sized crumbs
2. Add water, a tbsp at a time, stirring until pastry holds together, then chill for 20 minutes
3. Roll into a 10 inch circle on a floured surface—the ubiquitous floured surface, because I find in baking, there really is no other —and move to an ungreased baking sheet

Pies:
1. Slice and dice fruit very small
2. Combine fruit, flour, and sugar
3. Put filling in center of pastry and lift sides, partially covering fruit
1. Put butter on fruit still exposed (oh, my, is that legal!) in the middle
2. Bake 40 to 45 minutes, until the fruit is tender. Cool for at least 15 minutes before eating.

Rabbit Jerky

Bone four large rabbits and cut the meat into finger size strips, slicing with the grain. Marinate overnight in a brine solution with whatever spices you prefer. Sage, marjoram, allspice, celery seeds, basil, thyme, black pepper, cayenne pepper, nutmeg, cinnamon, tarragon, oregano, lemon or lime juice, garlic, rosemary, Tabasco, A-1 and Worcestershire are good in any combination. After marinating,

Nuts

Just for fun, we're going to assume the men with James Douglas got tired of nothing but Chillingham steak. They would have also eaten what the land provided. While they certainly did not have a copy of the *Liber Cure Cocorum* with them (hey, it was before the Gutenberg press, and they specialized in traveling light, anyway), they most certainly had some knowledge of living off the land.

Entrails of the woods [nuts]

Chawdewyne de boyce.
Take smalle notes, schale not kurnele,
As þou dose of almondes, fayre and wele;
Frye hom in oyle, þen sethe hom ry3t
In almonde mylke þat is bry3t;
Þen þou schalle do in floure of ryce
And also oþer pouder of spyce;
Fry oþer curneles besyde also,
Coloure þou hit with safron, or þou fer goo,
To divers þo mete þou schalt hit set,
With þo fryed curnels with outen let.
~ Liber Cure Cocorum

This is telling you to shell the nuts, fry them in oil, boil them (seethe means boil) in almond milk, add rice and spice, and color with saffron.

Book Four: WESTERING HOME

While I hate to give too much away, the premise of *Westering Home,* book four, is Shawn adjusting to life in the modern world. He is a much-changed man. But will the people who knew him accept those changes? Will he be able to maintain those changes in the face of those who loved the gambling, drinking, womanizing, party-throwing Shawn? The *fun* Shawn? How does a man who has gone raiding with James Douglas, who has just very deliberately killed a man in a tower, live among the powder blue polo shirts of modern men?

Niall, meanwhile, lives through the last half of 1316, and into 1317—years of continuing rain, famine, livestock disease, and continuing warfare, as Edward Bruce got Scotland involved in Ireland, fighting the English there.

History books tell us the dates, commanders, and outcomes of battles. The heart and soul of history lies in the human details: the day Robert the Bruce stopped an entire army, refusing to flee from the vastly superior oncoming army—for one of the women who served his army, cooking and cleaning, had gone into labor.

Niall is there to experience this remarkable event, with all the fear of watching the enemy surround them, while they stand, helpless against such vast numbers, but refusing to leave this woman alone. He is there to experience the very real and historical—the inexplicable—moment when this vast army turns and leaves, failing to engage Bruce's small and helpless force.

And Niall is there when a deserter from the English army tells Bruce exactly why the English left.

Niall is there to witness the horrible famine, worse in Ireland than anywhere else.

These, and more, are the backdrop of *Westering Home.*

Niall Drinking Whiskey After Battle

Allene studied the wound, running half the length of his upper arm, gaping with red, raw edges. "Whisky?" she asked, and promptly answered her own question. "Aye." She disappeared into the bed chamber and returned with a heavy flask, watching as Niall obediently downed half of it.

Scotch Drink Robert Burns

Let other poets raise a fracas
Bout vines and wines, and drunken Bacchus,
And crabbit names and stories wrack us,
And grate our lug:
I sing the juice Scotch bear can mak us,
In glass or jug

~ Robert Burns

History of Whisky/Scottish Whiskey

Whisky, in many minds, is nearly synonymous with Scotland. (Notice it is whisky in Scotland, not whiskey.) Considering the very word is dervied from the Gaelic *uisge*—as in *uisge-beatha,* water of life, whisky—this is hardly surprising. Indeed, so prominent is whiskey in Scottish culture that one Gaelic book teaches the phrase *tha mi ag iarriadh uisge-beatha*—I want whiskey—early on. I'm not making this up!

But records of the process—distilling fermented grains—date back to Mesopotamia and Babylon. The original process was used to create aromas and perfumes, but over time, the technique was refined to produce alcohol.

Some records suggest the early Celts distilled *uisge-beatha.* We know for sure that whiskey reached Scotland and Ireland, by way of the monks, by the 11th to 13th centuries. So Niall would certainly have had whisky to drink, and it *was* originally used as an internal anesthetic and an external antibiotic.

Whisky Drink

2 strawberries, hulled	1/2 oz. dry vermouth
1 strawberry slice for garnish	2 dashes aromatic bitters
1-3/4 oz. unaged whiskey	1/2 tsp fresh lemon juice
1/2 oz. Aperol	ice

1. Put strawberries, whiskey, Aperol, vermouth, bitters, lemon juice, and ice in a cocktail shaker
2. Rock, shake, rattle and roll, and shake that shaker well again
3. Strain into a chilled glass and garnish with a strawberry—unless you're in severe pain from a sword wound to the arm, or an arrow to the knee, in which case, I *strongly* suggest you gulp it down and ask for another

On cooking with whisky

While whisky's long-gone origins spring from perfumes and antiseptics, and is today regarded as a liquor (yes, it's true, you're paying a lot of money to drink antiseptic!) it is also used today in a surprising number of recipes from sauces to main dishes to desserts!

Whisky Cream Sauce

3 tbsp butter	dash of salt
1/2 C. onions, diced	pepper
1/2 C. whiskey	1/3 C. heavy cream
1/2 C. beef stock	

1. Saute onions in 2 tbsp butter over medium heat
2. When onions are brown, turn off burner—this is important!
3. Pour in whiskey. The moment it evaporates, turn the burner to medium-high heat and pour in beef stock.
4. Add salt and pepper and allow mixture to bubble up and reduce by half
5. Whisk in last tbsp of butter, then turn heat to low.
6. Whisk in cream; simmer and thicken for several minutes

You have a whisky cream sauce!

Whisky and Peach Chicken

PREHEAT OVEN: 350 degrees F

2 tbsp butter   1 C. peach preserves
2 tbsp olive oil   2 tbsp Worcestershire sauce
6 boneless chicken breasts   4 peaches, cut into 8 slices apiece
1 yellow onion, diced   3 green onions sliced thin
1-1/2 C. whisky   Fresh parsley, chopped
4 C. barbecue sauce

1. Heat butter and olive oil in a skillet over medium-high heat.
2. Add chicken; cook until golden brown on all sides and set aside.
3. Add onions to skillet; saute over medium heat until translucent
4. Add whisky—*be very careful over open flames!*
5. Cook for 3 minutes, allowing whisky to cook and reduce.
6. Whisk together barbecue sauce, peach preserves, Worcestershire sauce, and 1/2 cup water, return chicken to pan, and add peaches
7. Cover skillet; roast in oven until chicken is tender, 1-1/2 hours
8. Remove from oven and garnish with spring onions and parsley

Whisky Cookies

PREHEAT OVEN: 350 degrees F

1 C. brown sugar, packed firmly   1 lb pecan halves, 1/2 a lb chopped
1/2 C. butter   1 lb candied cherry
4 eggs   1 lb candied pineapple
3 C. flour   3 tbsp milk
1/2 tsp cinnamon   3 tsp baking soda
1/2 tsp clove   1/2 C. whisky
1/2 tsp nutmeg

1. Mix flour and spices; chop candied fruit into small pieces
2. Dredge chopped fruit and pecans through half a cup of flour
3. In a separate bowl, mix milk and baking soda
4. Blend together butter and sugar, and add eggs
5. Alternate adding a egg mixture, thenwhisky, into 2-1/2 cups flour
6. Mix in fruit and nuts
7. Use a small spoon to drop dough onto a greased cookie sheet
8. Bake 13 to 15 minutes

Chocolate Scotch Whisky Cake

PREHEAT OVEN: 375 degrees F

1/4 C. Scotch whisky
7 squares German sweet chocolate, chopped
1/2 C. butter
3 egg yolks
3 egg whites
2/3 C. white sugar

4-1/2 tbsp cake flour
2/3 finely ground almonds
a pinch of salt
3 squares German sweet chocolate, chopped
3 tbsp confectioners' sugar
3 tbsp butter

1. In a small bowl, combine raisins and scotch whiskey; set aside
2. Cut a circle of parchment paper to fit the bottom of the cake pan
3. Butter sides of pan and one side of the paper, and put the paper, butter side up, in the pan
4. Dust well with flour
5. In the top of a double boiler, combine 7 squares of chocolate and 3 tbsp of water
6. Stir until melted and smooth, then remove from heat and stir in 1/2 cup butter in small pieces
7. Beat egg yolks and sugar until pale creamy yellow, then add to chocolate
8. Combine flour and ground almonds and add to batter, then stir in the raisins and whiskey
9. In a clean bowl, whip egg whites and salt until stiff but not dry
10. Stir a third of the egg whites into the chocolate mixture
11. Fold chocolate mix into remaining egg whites and pour it all into the pan
12. Bake 20 minutes until outside is firm, center moist
13. Cool 10 minutes in pan; remove from pan to cool on cake rack for several hours or overnight. Remove parchment paper to frost.

Frosting:
1. Melt 3 oz. chocolate in the top of a double boiler
2. Stir in confectioners sugar, then 3 tbsp butter a little at a time and blend well
3. Frost cake immediately
4. Allow icing to set for about 30 minutes before serving

Breakfast After the Battle

"Tell me what happened, Christina," Allene said.

"We've men to see to," Christina said briskly. "The women will be up from the dungeons." She pushed the needle into a ball of thread, handing it to Allene. She smiled the mask of a smile, and swept from the room, calling back, "Come, your son will be needing you. And you need food and rest yourself, in your condition."

"I'll see to it," Allene said. She did indeed feel queasy. She followed Christina to the courtyard, where dawn turned the walls pink, and mist crawled along the ground. Men milled, talking, or drifted toward the great hall in hopes of food; only a few sat against the stone walls, in pain.

History

Sources vary on whether breakfast was common in the middle ages —never mind what was eaten or when. One source says breakfast was a leisurely affair eaten between six and seven, with white bread, three meat dishes, three dishes of fish, and wine or ale, while others say there were only two meals a day, with the first, eaten in late morning, being the main meal—which fits with Hildegard von Bingen belief that breakfast should be eaten late in the morning, and be served hot.

John of Milan and the Medical School of Salerno, advised, *Rise at 5, dine at 9, sup at 5, retire at 9, for a long life.*

It makes more sense to believe the second, since such a large meal, served at six in the morning, would require cooks to be working in the middle of the night. Of course, we know bakers do, so that's not impossible.

The answer is certainly that practices vary from one country to another, even one town or village to another, from century to century, from nobility to peasantry, and even among individual lords and castles. We know from our own time that we cannot make a blanket statement that breakfast is a leisurely affair eaten between 6 and 7. So some lords *may* have a large breakfast at six in the morning. Whether that was common is questionable.

Following are a few things they may have eaten.

Cheese

2 quarts milk   salt
1/4 C. vinegar   cream (for texture)

1. Heat milk slowly until it just starts to simmer—or to 195°F on a kitchen thermometer
2. Remove from heat, stir vinegar in gently, and let sit for 10 minutes
3. Strain through cheesecloth, wrap, and squeeze out as much whey as possible
4. Hang to drain for about an hour
5. Unwrap cheese and mix with salt and cream to desired flavor and texture
6. Mix in other herbs and spices as desired

Boiled Beef

For sirup.
Take befe and sklice hit fayre and thynne,
Of þo luddock with owte or ellis with in;
Take mynsud onyouns, and powder also
Of peper, and suet and befe þerto
And cast þeron, rolle hit wele,
Enbroche hit overtwert, so have þou cele;
And rost hit browne as I þe kenne,
And take brothe of fresshe flesshe þenne,
And alye hit with bred er þou more do,
And mynsud onyons þou cast þer to
With powder of peper and clowes in fere;
Boyle alle togeder, as I þe lere,
Þenne boylyd blode take þou shalle;
Strene hit þorowghe clothe, colour hit withalle;
Þenne take þy rost, and sklyce hit clene
In þe lengethe of a fynger; boyle hit by dene
In þe same sewe; serve hit þou may
In a disshe togedur I say.
~ Liber Cure Cocorum

The Lord's Bread: Pandemain (paindemaigne, paynemaine)

White bread was sometimes known as the lord's bread, as it was more expensive to make due to using the finest wheat flour and sifting three times to get rid of as much bran as possible.

And what did they do without yeast? Commoners might have used a sourdough starter, which was flour and water, left to stand and ferment with wild yeast—not the untamed kind (cue *Born to be wii—iii--ild!*) but the kind that exists in the air around us. Sourdough, however, was considered too common for the lord's bread. Ale barm—the froth skimmed off the top of fermenting ale—was also used.

Manchet Bread (white bread)

A medieval loaf would have been baked with about three times more flour than this recipe uses—presumably because it was serving at least three times as many people!

PREHEAT OVEN: 450 degrees F

3 C. white flour,
  unbleached stoneground
1 C. wholemeal bread flour,
  stoneground and sieved*

2 C. warm water
1 tsp sea salt, ground
1-1/2 tbsp active dried yeast**
1 tsp natural brown sugar

*OR 650 g traditional 80% extraction plain stoneground white bread flour from an artisan miller
** OR 3 tbsp fresh yeast

Yeast:
1. Pour half the warm water in a small bowl, dissolve sugar in it, sprinkle in yeast and stir well with with a plastic or wooden spoon
2. Leave in a warm place for 7 to 10 minutes in a warm place, checking occasionally to see if yeast is rising and frothing
3. After 4-5 minutes, it should be creamy and frothy on top. Do not let it sit longer than 12 minutes before using

For fresh yeast: use 3 tbsp with the same amount of sugar. It will take only half the time to activate

Bread:

1. Sift all flour together using a medium meshed sieve
2. Sprinkle in salt and mix with your fingers
3. Make a well in the flour
4. Pour activated yeast water into the well and stir it all together
5. If necessary, add more plain white flour until you have dough firm enough to knead and just a little sticky
6. Knead on a floured surface for about 7 minuets, adding flour to the surface as necessary to prevent sticking. Knead until it is satiny, elastic, and rises back when you push a finger into it
7. Roll into a ball, and return to floured bowl, cover with a clean, light cloth and leave in a warm room until it doubles in size— about 2 to 3 hours
8. Punch down and knead for 2 minutes
9. Roll back into a ball and set on a greased baking tray or a bread baking stone
10. Leave to rise again, 35 to 45 minutes
11. Cut a line in the top, not too deep, about 2 by 3 inches without depressing dough
12. Bake 10 minutes
13. Reduce temperature to 400 degree F and bake another 40 minutes, until it is brown and sounds hollow when tapped
14. Cool for one hour

Gruel of Almonds

Gruel of almondes.
Take almondes unblanchid and bray hom sone,
Put ote mele to, þenne hase þou done,
And grynde alle sammen and draw hit þenne
With water and sethe, as I þe kenne;
Coloure hit with safron and salt hit þenne,
And set in sale byfore gode menne.
~ Liber Cure Cocorum

History: Wine

Those of the medieval ages got their wine-making skills—as they got so many things—from the Romans, who inherited them in turn—as they did so many things—from the Greeks. A great deal of knowledge was lost after 400 A.D., with the decline of the Roman Empire. Wine-making skills, fortunately, were preserved by monks, in the making of their sacramental wine. In later years, they began making wine for their own enjoyment, too, which expanded to the nobility and from there began to regain popularity and spread to the general population.

By the end of the 11ᵗʰ century, there were 28 vineyards, that we know of, in Norman England. By the 1200s, medical texts were discussing the benefits of different wines—which we are only recently re-discovering.

Medieval wines were typically heavier and sweeter than modern wines.

Hildegard von Bingen's Wine List

Hildegard of Bingen recommended several interesting wines for illnesses of body and spirit:

- *Gold topaz wine*: Place a gold topaz in a glass of wine for three days. Moisten the eyelids once or twice a day, for five days, with the wine-moistened gold topaz. Repeat, with new wine, for at least three months. This cures cataracts, glaucoma, and bad eyesight.

- *Onyx wine*: Leave an onyx in a glass of wine overnight. The next day, boil the wine, with the stone still in it, f or 5 minutes. Remove the stone and drink the wine. This helps with swollen lymph glands and swollen spleen.

- *Parsley honey-wine*: Add 8 to 10 parsley leaves with stems, and 2 tbsp of wine vinegar to 1 quart of natural wine (red or white). Boil for 5 minutes. Add 3/4 C. of honey (1/3 C. less if you're diabetic) and boil for another 5 minutes. Skim off the foam, strain, and rebottle. 1 to 5 tbsp a day cures heart pain caused by weather and excitement, or by chronic rheumatic disease. It's also good after heart attacks.

If you try these and they work, let me know!

Sop in Wine

3 lbs blackberries   1 gal water
3 lbs sugar

1. Wash blackberries well and set aside in a large bowl
2. Boil water, pour over berries, and stir with a wooden spoon
3. Cover bowl with a towel and leave in a dry place, at room temperature
4. After 10 days, remove towel and peel away and discard mold that has formed
5. Cover bowl with muslin or cheesecloth, and pour juice through the cloth into another bowl
6. Add sugar and stir for a minute or two
7. Pour into wine bottles and cork them
8. Leave for at least three months before drinking—6 months would be better
9. On a sunny morning (or a cold, wintery one, your choice) at least three months from now, dip bread in wine, and happily dine

Like many others in this book, this is a fairly basic recipe, intended to show the basics of how things were done. The variations are really endless. Different fruits can be used, although this requires fruits with lower acid content—grapes and plums work well. Citrus peels and spices in various combinations, added to the fruit during the ten-day soak will give you a variety of flavors in your wine.

Fish Dish smoked herring, salmon, or trout

fish or meat   closed box, shed, or small room that can
                                hold in smoke and heat

Brining: It's best to brine first. Use a cup of salt for each gallon of liquid. Use enough liquid to cover the fish. Boil 2 cups of water per cup of salt needed. Boil. Stir in salt until dissolved. Add any other spices and herbs. Add in remaining—*cold*—liquid. Add any other brining ingredients you like, such as juice or fruit slices. *Brine must be cold before adding meat.*

Submerge the fish in cold brine. Fish must be completely covered. Refrigerate about an hour per pound of fish, or longer. The longer you brine, the stronger the flavor will be. Over-brining will result in very salty meat. No need to rinse. Begin smoking.

Salt is born of the purest of parents: the sun and the sea.
-Pythagoras

Cold Smoking: Keep temperature low, under 100 degrees F; under 80 is better. Fish lasts longer with cold smoking. At room temperature, it can last up to a week. The goal is not to cook the food, but to dry it.

Hot Smoking: Temperatures can be up to 250 degrees F. The aim is to cook the food, with a smoky flavor. Meats that are hot-smoked can be left out only a few days.

Smoking Outdoors: If no box, shed, or small room is available, smoke the fish or meat downwind of a smoking pile of coals. It will take a full day, or two if the weather is humid or still. When the meat becomes brittle, it is done.

The Wood:
- It should be somewhat green. If it is too dry, soak it

Woods to Use: Hardwood or fruit wood chips
- Applewood is good for poultry and pork
- Hickory wood gives hot, long-burning coals and rich, sharp flavor
- Maple wood chips are good for smoking meat, fish and cheese
- Mesquite—not be found by my medieval Scots—*would* be great for an earthy flavor if they could just wait 700 years.

Do not use:
- wood from trees that are toxic, including, but not limited to: black locust, yew, buckeye, horse chestnut, rhododendron, mountain laurel.
- bitter smoking resinous woods like cedar, cypress, redwood, fir, pine, spruce and other needle bearing trees.

The Meat:
- Cut into thin strips
- Drape over a framework
- None of the meat should touch any other piece

Breakfast Kippers

A kipper is a herring, gutted, split down the backbone, opened out, salted, and cold-smoked.

2 smoked undyed Scottish kippers	4 oz. double cream
16 oz. boiling water	1/2 lemon, juice only
1 oz. butter	salt and pepper
1 onion, finely chopped	3 hard-boiled eggs
1 tsp curry powder	3 tbsp chopped parsley
8 oz. basmati rice	

1. Peel and chop the eggs
2. Lay kippers in a deep baking dish and pour on boiling water
3. Leave for five minutes, then remove kippers, saving the liquid
4. Remove *all* bones from fish and set meat aside
5. Saute onions 3-4 minutes in butter until just softened but not browned
6. Sprinkle on curry powder and cook for another minute
7. Add rice, stir well into butter and onions
8. Add reserved liquid and heat to a simmer, then cover with a lid and cook 12-15 minutes, until all liquid is absorbed and rice is tender
9. Stir in cream and lemon juice
10. Season with salt and pepper, add kipper meat, eggs, and parsley, and stir gently

Niall Sings at Berwick

Food was scrounged from somewhere, despite heavy rains, and placed on the tables before Bruce's thousand men by young boys daring brave glances at the Scottish devils. The Black Douglas! they whispered. The gentle Jamie Douglas scared the English with the mere sound of his name.

Niall played and sang while the men ate, and the rain beat a harsh staccato against heavy lead glass in the windows high above. At his side, Conal harmonized in his soft tenor, though not as well as Iohn or Shawn, singing of lost love, battles heroically won, and battles tragically lost. Around them, men smiled for the first time in many weary weeks, as they sang the choruses.

A crust eaten in peace is better than a banquet partaken in anxiety.
- Aesop

Bough Cake

It is easy to imagine this being served at Berwick. Food would still have been scarce in this year of heavy rains and livestock disease. There would have been a massive influx of Douglas's men into Berwick. This is something they could have made for themselves over their campfires.

Batter:

1-1/4 C. flour   1/4 tsp salt
3/4 C. ale or beer   1 tbsp sugar or to taste
1/4 tsp saffron

1. Heat 3/4 cup ale or beer to lukewarm in a pan on the stove
2. Heat one tbsp of beer to hot and partially crush saffron into it
3. Mix with flour, salt and sugar, until smooth and thick
4. Set aside in a warm place to rise, 30 to 60 minutes

Bough Cake:

dried fruit—apricots, apples, plums, etc   batter
honey   spices

1. Thread dried fruit onto a long, thin stick—fruit shish kabob!
2. Coat with batter and roast over an open fire
3. Spoon more batter over fruit as it cooks, until they are covered in a thick layer
4. Roll bough cake in honey and spices

History: Ale

Tradition has it that ale was brought to England by the Romans—there are those Romans again—and improved by the Saxons. Ale is grain and water, fermented with yeast. One of our best sources for truly medieval ale is the household records of Elizabeth de Burgh—not to be confused with the Elizabeth de Burgh who married Robert the Bruce—whose household records give an idea of how ale was made in the 1330s—which would have been during Niall's lifetime, and only immediately after the death of Robert the Bruce.

One source believes that medieval ale would have typically been sweeter than today's ale. Like everything, of course, taste depends on many factors—locations, ingredients available, exact recipe, and more. Those ingredients might include oats, barley, rye, spelt, or wheat. (Hildegard of Bingen had a high regard for the health benefits of spelt, so this likely would have been her choice.) It might be flavored with any number of herbs: rose hips, yarrow, hyssop, savory, chamomile, purslane, mint, fennel, or—presumably while singing ancient melodies—parsley, sage, rosemary, and thyme. (I can guarantee I'd be singing if I were making ale with such herbs. I can guarantee I'd be singing it louder after a few large mugs of said ale!)

Ale was also flavored with spices—cinnamon, nutmeg, ginger, cloves, and cubeb. I can't help but notice that same group of spices, which Hildegard recommended for happiness, keeps popping up. So presumably using those spices would give us Hildegard's Ale of Joy. Then again, plenty of people find ale joyful anyway.

If you fear your ale will be too sweet, you might add juniper, mugwort, wormwood, or tansy.

See a method of making ale on p. 86

At the Pub with Zach and Kristen

Shawn watched them through the evening, as he gradually relaxed. A hot toddy helped, with its lemon floating in hot amber liquid, but it was more than that. Zach and Kristin either knew nothing of his prior reputation—which seemed unlikely in the sense of impossible—or didn't hold it against him, despite the fact that they were clearly not among those who would have found his antics amusing.

The Song

It's a wonder Shawn didn't burst into song at the pub. In many ways, life doesn't really change. People have always written songs and poems about food and drink, and we still do.

Ralph Flanagan fronted one of the 50s' most successful big bands. In 1953, he wrote the music for *Hot Toddy*, which quickly became a hit. It features a great trombone bass line, and I can easily imagine Shawn performing it over and over with his combo and having a blast doing so.

Herb Hendler wrote the lyrics, celebrating the joys of the hot toddy drink. Given the right spices, we would even have a Hot Toddy of Joy!

Hot Toddy

1-1/2 oz. brandy, whiskey, or rum	1 C. hot water
1 tbsp honey	1 tea bag
juice from 1/4 of a lemon	

1. Steep a tea bag in hot water 3 to 5 minutes
2. Fill coffee mug or glass with warm water until warm, then empty it
3. Coat mug/glass bottom with honey
4. Add liquor
5. Squeeze in lemon juice
6. Add steeped tea and stir.

Christmas Feast at Carrickfergus

The feasting lasted three days. Someone had hung sad, scanty boughs of evergreen. They were poor substitutes for Glenmirril's gaily decked halls, though their scent mingled tantalizingly with hundreds of wax tapers, and roasted venison carried in by streams of servants to the thousands of Scots filling the hall. He could almost forget the rain streaming down the windows and pattering in the courtyard, as the dishes kept coming, each smelling better than the last. "I thought there was famine here."

On the third day, Niall stood in the doorway of the great hall with Hugh, Owen, and Lachlan, wanting to be home, with one bird roasted inside another, a dozen sauces, fruits and nuts, and, most importantly, Allene and her father beside him. He surveyed the crowd of bearded men at Carrickfergus's tables. Gil Harper sat before Robert and Edward Bruce at the head table, singing lauds to the Scots. Candle and firelight flickered off the gold threads of the prancing lion on Bruce's tabard, and off the thin circlets of gold on the brothers' heads. "There's famine indeed." Beside them, the servant girl who had cared for Niall spoke softly in an Irish brogue. "We'll see it soon enough."

The History

The Christmas feast of 1316 at Carrickfergus must have been a poor one compared to most years. The previous 18 months or so had seen unusually heavy and frequent rains, in addition to an epidemic of livestock disease. Grain rotted in the fields. Animals died, taking with them their labor, meat, and milk. Edward Bruce had come to lead the Irish kings against their English oppressors. Between war, weather, and disease, 1315-1317 were years of famine all over year, but Ireland was hit especially hard.

On June 24, 1316, six months before Niall's Christmas feast at Carrickfergus, Edward Bruce was besieging the castle. He sent thirty Scots in to parley. Rather than negotiate, the Irish took them hostage. Reports said six (or eight) of them were killed—and eaten.

In September 1316, Edward Bruce took Carrickfergus.

It is against this backdrop that Edward and Robert Bruce scrounge up a Christmas feast. Not what Glenmirril had in good years, Niall thinks, and yet they managed to produce something. At least in my version. My guess is they would have had venison, maybe hare (is the world ever without rabbits?) and plenty of fish and things from the sea.

Glazed Fowl

6 slices of bacon chopped	2 C. ale
3 cloves of garlic, chopped	1/4 C. water
4 quail, pheasants, or Cornish hens	3 bay leaves, crumbled
1 C. chopped mushrooms	salt and pepper
1/2 tsp roasted hazelnuts	6 slices thick whole wheat bread

1. Chop bacon in large pieces; fry bacon and garlic in a heavy pot
2. Add birds; brown on all sides
3. Add nuts and mushrooms and cook for 5 minutes
4. Add ale, water, and bay leaves and bring to a boil
5. Cover and simmer for 2 to 2-1/2 hours, until meat is falling off the bones
6. Remove the birds
7. Cool juices completely; remove excess fat
8. When the birds are cool, remove the meat from the bones
9. Add meat back to the juices, reheating slowly
10. Serve on slices of bread

Go Day, Go Day, My Lord Syre Christemasse, go Day!

Medieval song

Good day, Syre Christemas, our kyng,
For every man, both olde & yinge,
Ys glad & blithe of your comynge;
Go day!
Go day, go day,
My lord Syre Christemasse, go day!

Godys sone so moche of myght
Ffram heven to erthe down is lyght
And borne ys of a mayde so bryght;
Good day!
Go day, go day,
My lord Syre Christemasse, go day!

Heven & erthe & also helle,
And alle that ever in hem dwelle,
Of your comynge they beth ful snelle;
Good day!
Go day, go day,
My lord Syre Christemasse, go day!

Of your comynge this clerkys fynde:
Ye come to save al mankynde
And of her balys hem unbynde;
Good day!
Go day, go day,
My lord Syre Christemasse, go day!

Alle maner of merthes we wole make
And solas to oure hertys take,
My semely lorde, for your sake;
Good day!

Venison Pie

*To bake Veneson. Take nothynge but pepper and salte, but lette it haue
ynoughe, and yf the Veneson be leane, larde it throughe wyth bacon.*

*Venyson ybake. Take hanches of Venyson, parboile it in faire water and
salt; then take faire paast, and ley there-on the Venyson y-cutte in pieces
as thou wolt have it, and cast vnder hit, and aboue hit, powder of ginger,
or peper and salt medylde togidre, And sette hem in An oven, and lete
hem bake til they be ynogh.*
                          ~ Harleian Manuscripts

PREHEAT OVEN: 350 degrees F

2 lbs ground venison   ginger
1/2 lb chopped bacon   grains of paradise
salt and pepper   pie crust

1. Mix ground venison and spices and put into the pie crust
2. Bake about 45-50 minutes

For to make a pottage of oysters

For to make a potage of oysturs.

*Perboyle þyn oysturs and take hom oute;
Kepe welle þy bre with outen doute,
And hakke hem on a borde full smalle,
And bray in a morter þou schalle;
Do hom in hor owne brothe for goode,
Do mylke of almondes þer to by þe rode,
And lye hit up with amydone,
And frye smalle mynsud onyone
In oyle, or sethe hom in mylke þou schalle;
Do powdur þerto of spyces withalle,
And coloure hit þenne with safron gode;
Hit is holden restoratyf fode.*
                          ~ Liber Cure Cocorum

Porpoise Frumenty

Dolphins can be seen today in the vicinity of Carrickfergus today and no doubt could be then, too. *Forme of Cury* leaves us a porpoise frumenty—a frumenty being made from boiled cracked wheat, *frumentum* being Latin for grain. Frumenty generally involved milk, eggs, or broth, and various recipes included almonds, currants, saffron and meat of some type.

Dolphin counted as fish, so porpoise frumenty could be eaten during Lent. It was also used as a subtlety. Therefore, with creatures of the sea being more available, it seems a likely choice for the Carrickfergus feast of 1316.

Porpoise frumenty is completely illegal today. Not to mention, I think most westerners are as likely to eat Flipper as Lassie.

Take clene whete and bete it small in a morter and fanne out clene the dust. Waisthe it and boile it tyl it be tendre. Take the mylk of Almonds & boile them. Take up the porpays out of the Furmente & leshe hem in a dishe with hot water.
~ Forme of Cury

Pokerounce

This, my secret sources say, and always alliteratively, was a favorite medieval dish. I can see why, because clearly *pokerounce* is middle English for *boys playing with food*. Many readers have likely eaten something very like this already, without realizing it was a medieval treat. It's simple enough, I think Carrickfergus could have provided this even in a famine.

4 thick slices of white bread   pinch each: ginger, cinnamon, pepper
8 oz. honey   1/2 oz. pine nut kernels

1. Toast bread and cut into small squares.
2. Melt honey in a pan with spices—no more than two minutes
3. Pour honey over the toast, then stand pine-nut kernels upright in honey, like little chess men or soldiers. Serve hot.

Hedgehogs in Wild Duck Sauce

Le Managier de Paris, the goodman of Paris tells his young wife how to prepare a hedgehog. This time, we're talking about a real hedgehog, not a subtlety. He advises dropping it in hot water if it refuses to uncurl itself. Then, after the basic instructions on slaughtering and preparing an animal, he recommends serving hedgehog with cameline sauce **(p 169)** or in a pastry with wild duck sauce. Hm—sounds like the same sauces recommended for squirrel! Here's the wild duck sauce:

2/3 C. verjuice	1/4 tsp cloves
1/3 C. red wine vinegar	1/4 tsp nutmeg
1/4 tsp cinnamon (cassia)	1/4 tsp mace
1/2 tsp ginger	1/8 tsp pepper
1 tsp galingal*	

* Galingal is called for in many medieval recipes, but not often found in local grocery stores. It is a member of the ginger family, so substituting ginger will give you something very like *Le Managier's* wild duck sauce.

1. Mix together well, add to pre-cooked meat and bring to a boil
2. Simmer for 20 minutes

Ermine

Ermine. Hit schal beon ymad qwit & wel ysauoured of god poudre of gynger & quibibes & cloues, & þis mete schal beon perti wiþ vert desire.

In short, it should be well-savored with ginger, cubebs, and cloves

Lamprey in Hot Sauce

From *Le Viandier de Taillevent*

lamprey	ginger
toast	cassia cinnamon (or regular cinnamon)
vinegar	cloves
red wine	grains of paradise
nutmeg	

1. Bleed lamprey through the mouth; remove tongue; save blood
2. Scald the lamprey and thread it crosswise on a thin spit to form one or two loops, and roast it
3. Mix the blood with vinegar and a little wine and soak toast in it
4. Grind soaked toast with ginger, cassia cinnamon, cloves, grains of paradise, and nutmeg, then steep it all and bring to a boil
5. Immediately add the lamprey whole
6. A thick sauce should be black; a clear sauce should not be

Alternately, some castle cooks preferred to serve the lamprey and sauce separately, with the lamprey cut lengthwise in pieces and the sauce served on the side.

Birds roasted inside Birds

History of Engastration

Although engastration—the cooking of animals inside other animals —goes back at least to Roman times (there are those Romans *again)* birds roasted inside birds is particularly medieval—one of the great show dishes. A wide variety of birds were used in this showcase culinary delight. In what is possibly the most famous instance, in 1807, Grimod de la Reynière created his *rôti sans pareil*, the roast without equal: a warbler in a bunting in a lark in a thrush in a quail in a lapwing in a plover in a partridge in a woodcock in a teal in a guinea fowl in a duck in a chicken in a pheasant in a goose in a turkey—and all of it inside the great bustard.

Creative minds being what they are, there is no doubt birds other than this have been used! But Grimod settled for only 17!

The basic premise of the bird within a bird is to layer birds with stuffing.

STUFFINGS

Andoullie

3 lbs coarsely ground pork
1 1/2 tsp chopped garlic
1 tsp kosher salt
1/2 tsp paprika
1/4 tsp black pepper
1/4 tsp dried thyme
1 pinch chili pepper flakes

pinch ground mace
pinch ground allspice
pinch ground bay leaf
pinch ground sage
pinch cayenne pepper, optional
3 tsp bacon fat

1. Mix all ingredients except bacon fat with cold water, then brown in bacon fat, then chill! (The stuffing, not you.)

Spinach: saute the following in melted butter and let cool:

1/2 lb butter
3 lbs fresh spinach, chopped
2 C. sauteed onion

1 tsp ground fennel seed
1 tsp kosher salt
1/2 tsp white pepper

Sausage and berries: mix together thoroughly:

1/2 lb sausage meat
3/4 C. of cranberries, semi-dried

3/4 C. walnuts, chopped
1 tsp juniper berries, crushed

Nuts

6-10 mushrooms
1 onion
3/4 C. pinenuts, crushed
1-1/2 C. pork sausages, skinless

zest of 1 lemon
handful of thyme
handful of parsley
spoonful of breadcrumbs

1. Chop onion and mushrooms very fine.
2. Saute onion in butter for two minutes, add mushrooms
3. Mix all the other stuffing ingredients together
4. Add onions and mushrooms and mix together well

BIRDS

pheasant	duck	partridge
chicken	grouse	

De-bone birds, leaving the legs only on the largest.
For the largest bird only: leave wings attached to meat; the bone-in drumstick should be disjointed from the boneless thigh meat but left attached, for a flat boneless turkey, except for wings and drumsticks.

Layer Birds and Stuffing:
1. Place largest bird skin-side down on a flat surface. Rub meat with 3 tbsp olive oil. Sprinkle with chopped fresh garlic
2. Spread a thin layer of dressing (your choice) over meat; pat it down
3. On top, place 6 to 8 slices of roasted red bell peppers
4. Put second largest bird, skin-side down, on top of layered stuffing
5. Spread another layer of (different) stuffing
6. Repeat with progressively smaller birds and different stuffings
7. Spread the last of the stuffing on top of smallest bird.
8. Press   down,   compacting   all   ingredients

Truss the Outer Bird:
1. Lift sides of the outermost bird together, with help
2. Start at the back of the bird and work toward the neck, sewing together with butcher's twine, the stitches about an inch apart
3. Roll the bird over and sew up the neck
4. Sew the leg sections closed and tie the legs together
5. Tie butcher's twin around the bird about every three inches, the full length of the bird for more support.

Into the Roaster:
1. Sprinkle shallots, thyme, carrot, and the remaining legs and wing tips in a roasting pan
2. Place bird on vegetables and rub all over with softened butter
3. Pour wine over it all (really, shouldn't this just be standard in cooking, and in life?)
4. Cover loosely with a foil dome
5. Cook: 2.5 hrs in water bath, 167F, then 350F for 1 to 1-1/2 hrs OR 325 F for 2 to 3 hrs, then 350 F for 1 to 1-1/2 hrs

Blackfriars Pub: Scottish Pub Recipes

"We've been at this ten years now," Clive said. "You may as well tell me. She's persistent, is she not?"

"Not as persistent as you." Angus scanned the scouts' dates, and accepted.

"'Twas was a good idea on her part," Clive persisted, "Get to know each other a bit before you spend a whole day together at the Games."

"Mmhm." Angus typed an e-mail to the chief, telling him about the speaking engagement in September.

"A big band at Blackfriars, she told the girls out front. Nice place."

"Lot of history there," Angus murmured.

"I'm sure she knew that would appeal to you." Clive brushed at the donut crumbs on his uniform.

Angus opened the e-mail from the pipe band. A performance at Glenmirril. He'd developed mixed feelings about the place. But he'd always loved the castle, and he loved playing. Sounds grand, he typed. I'll be there. He'd have to get the kilt to the cleaners and practice a little. It had been awhile. It stung that Amy had looked forward to seeing him play, and now she wouldn't be there.

"She's a nice girl," Clive continued.

"So you said." Angus noted the speaking engagement and pipe band gigs on the calendar on his desk.

"Did you kiss her?"

"Ah, fer feck's sake, Chisolm!" Angus slammed the pen down. His head shot up. "I didn't kiss her, I didn't sleep with her, I didn't hold her hand. I didn't want to go out with her or anyone in the first place."

"Which is exactly why you should, instead of moping about. She's a nice girl."

Fish and Chips

PREHEAT OVEN: 450 degrees F/ FRYER OIL: 325 degrees F

Fish:

1 lb skinless haddock	pinch of salt
6 oz. all purpose flour	beer
1/2 oz. baking powder	

1. Cut fish into large pieces
2. Sift flour and baking powder together into a bowl; add salt
3. Add beer a bit at a time, to form a smooth, medium-thick batter
4. Dip each fish piece in batter
5. Fry 8 to 10 minutes each, to golden and crispy; do not use a basket
6. Lay on paper towel-lined plate

Chips:

4 medium potatoes	coarse ground pepper
a bit of olive oil	coarse sea salt

1. Slice potatoes into 'fries' then toss with olive oil, salt, and pepper
2. Bake for 20 minutes.

Scones

PREHEAT OVEN: 400 degrees F

1-3/4 C. all-purpose flour	1/2 C. dried currants or raisins
4 tsp baking powder	1/2 C. milk
1/4 C. white sugar	1/4 C. sour cream
1/8 tsp salt	1 egg
5 tbsp unsalted butter	1 tbsp milk

1. Sift flour, baking powder, sugar and salt together in a bowl
2. Cut in butter, into pea sized lumps, and stir in currants
3. Combine 1/2 cup milk and sour cream, then add to flour mixture
4. Stir gently until well-blended but....*do not overdo it!*
5. With floured hands, roll dough into 2 to 3 inch balls
6. Set on a greased baking sheet and flatten a little—the scones should barely touch each other
7. Whisk egg and 1 tbsp of milk together
8. Use milk/egg to brush top of dough; let them rest for 10 minutes.
9. Bake 10 to 15 minutes, until tops are golden brown

Scotch Eggs

HEAT OIL IN FRYER: 375 degrees F

1 egg	1 tbsp dried parsley, crushed
1 C. mayonnaise	2 tsp grated lemon zest
1/4 C. yellow mustard	1/4 tsp ground nutmeg
2 tbsp white sugar	1/4 tsp dried marjoram
6 hard boiled eggs, peeled	salt and pepper to taste
2 qt oil for deep frying	1 egg, beaten
12 oz. ground pork sausage	

Mustard sauce:
1. Over low heat, mix together egg, mayonnaise, mustard and sugar, until it just starts to boil
2. Remove, let cool, then chill for 10 minutes or more

Eggs:
1. Mix well with hands: sausage, parsley, lemon rind, nutmeg, marjoram, salt and pepper
2. Coat each hard boiled egg with sausage mix, using wet hands to get an even layer
3. Roll coated eggs in beaten egg, then in breadcrumbs
4. Slide 3 eggs into fryer and fry 4 to 5 minutes, turning at least once to brown evenly, until they are deep golden brown
5. Remove with slotted spoon, and set on paper towel-lined plate while frying the next 3

Cullen Skink

2 lbs smoked haddock fillets   2 large potatoes, peeled and diced
2 1/2 C. milk   black pepper to taste
1 large onion, finely chopped   2 tbsp fresh parsley, chopped

1. Simmer haddock and milk over medium heat for about 15 minutes, until fish flakes easily with a fork
2. Remove fish and set aside
3. Add potatoes and onion to milk; simmer until tender, about 10 minutes
4. Pour milk and potatoes into a blender, in batches if needed; blend until smooth and creamy and return to pan (both you and the milk/potatoes should return to the pan—it does no good if you don't also go)
5. Flake fish into soup and heat gently—do not boil
6. Season with pepper and garnish with parsley

Clootie Dumpling

4 oz. margarine   1 tsp each ground cinnamon
2-1/2 C. flour   1 tsp mixed spice*
1-1/2 C. oatmeal   1 tsp light corn syrup
1/2 C. sugar   2 eggs, beaten
8 oz. currants/ sultanas/ raisins   3/4 tbsp buttermilk
rounded tsp baking powder

*Mixed spice is common to British cooking, particularly for Christmas food, hot cross buns, and baked goods. There are many recipes for mixed spice (Are you surprised at this point!) which typically involve cinnamon, coriander, caraway, nutmeg, ginger, cloves, allspice, and mace. Not too specific, is it? Pumpkin pie spice mix is a substitute. To make your own genuine mixed spice, here are two recipes:

- 1 tbsp each: ground allspice, ground cinnamon, nutmeg; 2 tsp ground mace; 1 tsp each ground cloves, ground coriander, ground ginger
- 1 tbsp each: cinnamon, nutmeg, allspice; 2 tsp mace; 1 tsp ground cloves

Now that you have mixed spice:

1. Sift flour into bowl, mix in margarine, add other dry ingredients
2. Make a well in the center, add syrup and eggs and mix well (notice these recipes never say mix *poorly*? I'm not much of a cook, I freely admit, but is there ever a time to mix poorly?)
3. Add buttermilk slowly until you have a batter soft...yet firm
4. [At Christmas, wrap a coin in wax paper inside the dumpling]
5. Traditionally: Dip a cloth in boiling water, flour it well, put clootie mixture in the middle and tie the top, leaving room for expansion. Place a saucer in the bottom of a saucepan, set the dumpling-in-cloth on it, cover with boiling water, and simmer 2 to 3 hours OR: Use an 8 cup basin or a lightly greased pudding steamer; leave an inch free above the batter; cover steamer or basin with a greased sheet of tin foil, pour boiling water in two-thirds up the side, and boil for 3 hours.
6. Remove dumpling(s); serve hot with custard or cold with cream

Bubble and Squeak

1 lb potatoes, peeled and cut 1 tsp prepared yellow mustard
2 C. shredded cabbage   1/2 C. shredded Cheddar cheese
1 carrot, grated   salt and pepper to taste
1 onion, minced

1. Bring potatoes to a boil, then simmer until tender, 10 minutes.
2. Boil 'em, mash 'em, stick 'em in a....I mean, drain, mash, set aside
3. Put cabbage and carrot in another pan
4. Add just enough water to cover bottom of pan
5. Cook on medium until tender, then drain and stir into potatoes
6. Add onion, mustard, and Cheddar cheese, salt, and pepper
7. Shape mixture into 4 patties and set on a greased grill pan
8. Grill on medium-high until golden brown, 5 minutes on each side

Minced Pie

PREHEAT OVEN: 275 degrees F

Meat Filling: *Hot Water Pastry:*
1 lb lean lamb, ground   4 C. plain flour
pinch of mace or nutmeg   3/4 C. lard
salt and pepper   3/4 C. water
1/4 pt gravy   pinch of salt

You will also need: a glass or jar 3 inches in diameter and milk for glazing

1. Mix lamb, spice and seasoning for filling
2. For pastry, sift flour and salt into a warm bowl
3. Make a well in the center of the flour
4. Melt lard in a little water and when it is bubbling, add to flour and mix well
5. Using about 3/4 of the pastry, make 8 to 10 pie crusts, each about 3 to 3-1/2 inches in diameter, with the bottom of the glass. As pastry cools, remove glass and make more
6. Fill pastries with the meat, adding gravy to moisten
7. Roll out remaining pastry and use the glass to cut the lids
8. Wet edges of lids, place over the meat, and press down over filling; seal edges and trim, and pierce vent holes in each lid
9. Glaze with milk and bake about 45 minutes

Helen and Simon at the Pub

"Niall Campbell," Simon mused, when she'd gone. "A fourteenth century inhabitant of Glenmirril, was he not?"

"Aye." Helen stabbed a fork into her haggis. "How an American knew such an obscure historical figure was a matter of much speculation. His father, they say, loved Scottish history, so 'tis possible...."

"After he awoke calling himself Niall Campbell?" Simon cut off her blathering, not interested in her erroneous speculation. She'd no clue what had really transpired. "After that?"

She looked at him, her fork in her dinner. "His obsession with Bannockburn. They say he was mad, researching, printing up maps of the battle and grounds. Amy took him to the Trossachs. I don't understand why she'd have done, when 'twas so clear he wasn't right in the head."

"The Trossachs, rather than Bannockburn," Simon said. "Why?"

"To find a man named Hugh."

"Malcolm MacDonald's brother." Simon dug into his chicken. Juices ran down his chin. He wiped them with the back of his hand.

Traditional Haggis

1 sheep's stomach bag	3/4 C. oatmeal
1 sheep's pluck - liver, lungs, heart	salt and black pepper
3 onions	pinch of cayenne
1 C. beef suet	5 oz. stock/gravy

1. Clean stomach well; soak overnight and in the morning turn it inside out
2. Wash the pluck, then boil 1-1/2 hours, hanging windpipe over the pot to drain
3. Mince heart and lungs and grate half the liver.
4. Chop onions and suet, and warm oatmeal in oven
5. Mix oatmeal, onions, suet, heart, lungs, and liver togethe, season with salt, pepper, and cayenne
6. Pour enough of the pluck boiled water over the oatmeal mixture to make it watery
7. Fill bag half full with mixture, press out air; sew the bag up
8. Boil 3 hours without a lid; prick with a knife to vent, if necessary

Traditional Haggis

1/2 lb liver in a piece	4 oz. chopped suet
1/2 lb cooked tripe	4 oz. chopped onion
4 oz. fine oatmeal	salt and pepper

1. Using just enough water to cover it, boil liver 15 minutes
2. Mince liver and cooked tripe, then mix all ingredients; salt and pepper
3. Using the water in which liver was cooked, make a moist dough
4. Wrap it in a pudding cloth and boil it for two hours or steam it in a bowl for three hours

Chicken

PREHEAT OVEN: 350 degrees F

3 lb boneless, skinless chicken	1 tbsp soy sauce
1 tbsp apricot jam	pinch of Cayenne pepper
1 tsp Dijon mustard	large clove of crushed garlic
3 tbsp tomato ketchup	salt and pepper to taste
1 tbsp Worcestershire sauce	

1. Season chicken and spread in a pan
2. Mix jam, mustard, pepper and garlic until smooth.
3. Add ketchup, Worcestershire sauce, soy sauce, salt and pepper
4. Pour over chicken pieces, coating evenly
5. Cover and bake for one hour.

Niall Feeds Hugh at Adair

Niall smiled sadly. Yes, God had granted them refuge. A cool breeze blew through the stone casement behind him, into the stifling sick room.

"Will I pull the shutters?" Roysia glanced out at the stars twinkling against the black sky.

Niall shook his head. Shawn had been big on fresh air.

In the bed, Hugh stirred, and opened his eyes. He gazed at the hangings for a moment, before turning to Niall.

"Roysia has brought you soup." Niall grinned. "But you'll have to stop lying about, and sit up."

With a groan, and some help from Niall, Hugh managed to pull himself upright against the pillows. But his hands shook so that Niall lifted the spoon for him.

"I'm away to Douglas at dawn," he said, as Hugh sipped. "You and Roysia will bide here. My Lord Adair will care well for you."

"Where will he find food for two more?" Hugh whispered. Even his voice was weak and thin compared to his former robustness.

"We're on the Irish Sea," Niall replied. "It provides well."

The nourishment of body is food, while the nourishment of the soul is feeding others.

~ Alī ibn Abī Ṭālib, Caliph

Song of the Zetland Fishermen, Sir Walter Scott

Farewell, merry maidens, to song, and to laugh,
For the brave lads of Westra are bound to the Haaf;
And we must have labour, and hunger, and pain,
Ere we dance with the maids of Dunrossness again.

For now, in our trim boats of Noroway deal,
We must dance on the waves, with the porpoise and seal
The breeze it shall pipe, so it pipe not too high,
And the gull be our songstress whene'er she flits by.

Sing on, my brave bird, while we follow, like thee,
By bank, shoal, and quicksand, the swarms of the sea;
And when twenty-score fishes are straining our line,
Sing louder, brave bird, for their spoils shall be thine.

We'll sing while we bait, and we'll sing while we haul
For the deeps of the Haaf have enough for us all:
There is torsk for the gentle, and skate for the carle,
And there's wealth for bold Magnus, the son of the earl.

Huzza! my brave comrades, give way for the Haaf,
We shall sooner come back to the dance and the laugh;
For life without mirth is a lamp without oil;
Then, mirth and long life to the bold Magnus Troil!

History

Fish was a major part of the medieval Scottish diet, in part because it was plentiful—in the ocean, lochs, inland streams, and even fish ponds on feudal lands—and in part due to Church regulations which declared Fridays, all of Lent, and certain other days meatless.

The variety of seafood was vast: pike (a favorite), plaice, flounder, oysters, cockles, scallops, whelks, herring, salmon, trout, mackerel, tuna, shrimp, lamprey, eel, anchovies, sardines, cod (but beware if your recipe calls for cod pieces!), carp—and even dolphin (yes, dolphins were considered fish).

The stew below, like an recipe, can have pretty much whatever you want in it. Don't limit yourself to what's listed. Have fun!

Hildegard on Fish

Hildegard von Bingen regarded several types of fish as particularly healthy: grayling, trout, bass, cod, pike, wels catfish, pike perch. She regarded eel, crabs, tench, and plaice to be bad. If you ever suffer pain from eating fried fish (or fried anything), she recommended eating fennel or fennel seeds to reduce the pain.

Adair's Seaside Stew

2 C. flaked fish	salt and pepper
4 frog legs	1/2 tsp rosemary
2 leeks, diced	enough water to cover it all
2 tbsp chopped onion	2 oz. butter
1/2 C. mushrooms	

1. Simmer fish for 15 minutes
2. In a separate pan, saute leeks and minced onion in butter
3. Add mushrooms and rosemary and saute another minute or two
4. Remove cooked vegetables to a pot with water; set to simmer over medium heat
5. Add leftover butter and frog legs; sprinkle with salt and pepper
6. Cook frog legs until meat falls off bone; transfer to the broth with the sautéed vegetables
7. Simmer 10 minutes

Adair's cooks, of course, would have put in any seafood they had on hand, and you should, too!

Blancmange of fish

Blanc maungere of fysshe.
Take a pownde of ryse and sethe hom wele,
Tyl þat þay brostene; and lete hom kele.
Mylke of almondes þerto þou cast,
Þo tenche or lampray do to on last;
Welle alle togeder, as I þe kenne,
And messe hit forthe before godde men
~ Liber Cure Cocorum

Mortrews of fish

Mortrews of fysshe.
Take þo kelkes of fysshe anon,
And þo lyver of þo fysshe, sethe hom alon;
Þen take brede and peper and ale,
And temper þo brothe fulle welle þou schalle,
And welle hit togeder and serve hit þenne,
And set in sale before good mene
~ Liber Cure Cocorum

Lampreys in broth

Lamprayes in browet.
Take lamprayes and scalde hom by kynde,
Sythyn, rost hom on gredyl, and grynde
Peper and safrone; welle hit with alle,
Do þo lampreyes and serve hit in sale
~Liber Cure Cocorum

Lampreys in [sauce]

Lamprayes in galentine.
Take lamprayes and hom let blode
At þo navel, and scalde hom for gode;
Rost home þenne, and þou hom laye
Alle hole in platere, as I þe saye;
Serve with galentine, made in sale,
With gyngere, canel and galingale
~ Liber Cure Cocorum

For to make a pottage of whelks

For to make a potage of welkes.
Take welkes and wasshe fayre, in blythe,
In water, and take whyte salt þerwith
And after hakke hom on a borde,
As smalle as þou may, at a worde,
And bray hom in a morter clere;
Sethe hom in mylke over þe fyre;
Of almondes or of a clow þou take schalle,
Lye hit with amydone þerwith alle;
Coloure hit with safrone, and do þerinne
Poudur of peper, or goode comyne.
~Liber Cure Cocorum

Feast at Lintalee

Within days, the house was finished. His heart light with the prospect of the night's feasting and entertainment, and heading home the next day to Allene, Niall entered the great hall with Lachlan and Owen. Serving boys poured in, setting out steaming platters of meat and bread. Douglas's men flocked to wooden benches, pounded trestle tables, and shouted for ale. A man juggled small burlap balls stuffed with straw, until he tripped over one of Douglas's shaggy hounds, and the balls showered down around him. He grinned at the laughter and ribbing showering down with them. The dog woofed, skittered in the rushes, and licked the man's face.

Amidst the laughter, the door crashed open. A messenger exploded into the ribaldry. "My Lord!" He paused, breathing hard, hands on knees, before looking up, in search of Douglas's height and head of black hair. "Arundel is coming to take down Jedburgh forest," he gasped.

History

"James Douglas? I don't even know who that is!" snaps one of the orchestra's board of directors at Shawn, on his arrival back in modern times.
"That's a shame," Shawn responds. *"He was a great man."*

It's probably no surprise that I agree with Shawn. Well, maybe it is. I certainly don't agree with him—or Simon—on many of his feelings and attitudes! But I do agree with him on this.

Hush ye, hush ye, do not fret ye,
The Black Douglas will not get thee

This was a lullabye sung to English children from the days of James Douglas's raids in England, for centuries onward. One story tells of a woman singing it to her child, during James's re-taking of Roxburgh Castle. As she sang *The Black Douglas will not get thee,* a leather-gloved hand slid around her mouth as James himself said, "I wouldn't be so sure of that." Another version of the story I've heard—and prefer—is that James said, "Not tonight, at least."

How is it that a man whose name became a bogeyman feared by English children was known as *The Good Sir James* to others? How is it that seven hundred years later, he continues to have so many admirers?

He was Robert the Bruce's close friend and right hand man, left in charge of Scotland while Robert went to Ireland with his brother Edward. He is portrayed, historically, as a gentle and even soft-spoken man, until he got on a battlefield, at which point it was best to be his friend, and not his enemy.

He is largely responsible for the years-long series of raids into Northern England, which were a key part of the Scots' strategy to convince Edward I it was to his people's benefit—if not his own—to sign a peace treaty.

In 1316-17, just two years after Bannockburn, he built his home at Lintalee, just south of Jedburgh, close to the English border. Edmund Fitzalan, Earl of Arundel, decided he would clear the forests near James's new home, which had long sheltered James and his merry men.

Instead, James pulled off another of his famous routs, decimating Arundel's troops. On returning home, he found more of Arundel's men eating his housewarming feast! He decimated them, too. Do not crash James Douglas's house parties!

In Praise of Claret, William Hamilton of Gilbertfield 1665-1751

The dull draff-drink maks me sae dowff
A' I can do's but bark and yowff
Yet set me in a claret howff
Wi' folk that's chancy,
My muse may len' me then a gowff
To clear my fancy.
Then Bacchus-like I'd bawl and bluster
And a' the Muses 'bout me muster
Sae merrily I'd squeeze the cluster
And drink the grape
'T wad gi'e my verse a brighter lustre
And better shape.

Draff-drink = inferior whisky
dowff = dull, spiritless
yowff = give short, sharp barks

howff = a haunt, resort, tavern
chancy = lucky, bringing good luck
gowff = blow, cuff

Clarrey (Wine with honey and spices)

There are rivers great and fine
Of oil, milk, honey and wine;
~ The Land of Cokaygne, c. 1330

Clarrey. Take kanel & galinga, greyns de paris, and a lytel peper, &
make pouder, & temper hit wyt god wyte wyne & the þrid perte honey &
ryne hit þorow a cloþ.
~ 14th century Forme of Cury

1 tsp cinnamon
1/4 tsp galingale
1/2 tsp grains of paradise
pinch of pepper

1 bottle white wine
1/3 C. + 2 tbsp honey
5 tbsp water

1. Bring honey and water to a boil, skimming if needed
2. Add spices cool, add wine, cover and let sit at least 15 minutes
3. Strain repeatedly through a sieve lined with fine cloth until clear
4. Return wine to original bottle
5. Set bottle upright in cool place, at least one day; handle gently so as not to stir up dregs

Red And White Medieval Gingerbread

Red and White Gingerbreads were popular in medieval times. Gingerbread was a simple mix of breadcrumbs with honey, pepper, saffron and cinnamon. The observant reader (and I assume you all are!) will note that ginger is not listed for the *ginger* bread. It was not listed in the very earliest recipe we have—a medieval typo? Ours will have ginger.

Take a quart of hony, & sethe it, & skeme it clene; take Safroun, poudir Pepir & throw ther-on; take gratyd Brede & make it so chargeaunt (thick) that it wol be y-leched; then take pouder Canelle (cinnamon) & straw ther-on y-now; then make yt square, lyke as thou wolt leche yt; take when thou lechyst hyt, an caste Box (garden box) leves a-bouyn, y-stkyd ther-on, on clowys (cloves).
~ Harleian MS. 279 , fifteenth century cookbook

1 lb honey	2 tsp ground ginger
powdered saffron	2 tsp ground cinnamon
cloves	1 lb white breadcrumbs
black pepper	box or bay leaves

1. Warm honey over low heat until it is runny
2. Stir in saffron and pepper
3. Pour into a bowl; add ginger and cinnamon
4. Mix in enough breadcrumbs to make a stiff mixture
5. Spread mixture in a pan; modern readers are advised to line the pan with wax or parchment paper
6. Cool for several hours in a cold place in your castle, or, if you're fortunate enough to have one, a mechanical cooling box
7. Remove from pan and cut into small squares
8. Decorate squares with box or bay leaves and stick a whole clove in the middle of each
9. And if thou wolt have it Red, coloure it with Saunderys (sandalwood) y-now: use sandalwood—or, in modern times, red food dye

Herb And Flower Salad

From 1390, this is the earliest known 'recipe' for salad. It may seem silly to have a 'recipe' per se, but it is interesting to see that salad was not merely a collection of greens and fresh vegetables, but a work of art.

Take persel (parsley), sawge, grene garlec, chibolles (spring onions), oynouns, leek, borage, myntes, porrettes, fennel, and town cressis, rew, rosemaye, purslayne; lave and wasche hem clene. Pike hem. Pluk hem small with thyme hande, and mingle hem wel with rawe oile; lay on vynegar and salt, and serve it forth.

~ 14ᵗʰ century, Forme of Cury

2 lbs watercress	1 oz. daisy leaves, chopped
mustard greens and cress	red sage leaves
3 fresh parsley sprigs	mint leaves
1 leek finely sliced	1 fresh rosemary sprig
6 spring onions chopped	1 clove garlic
1 oz. sorrel leaves, chopped	1 tbsp wine vinegar
1 oz. dandelion leaves, chopped	salt and pepper
1 fennel bulb, sliced thin	6 tbsp olive oil

assortment of flowers to decorate: violets, primrose, daisies, blue borage flowers, dandelions and alexander buds

1. Wash and dry salad greens
2. Rub a large bowl with a garlic clove; toss greens in it
3. Put wine vinegar, seasonings and olive oil into a bottle and shake well—really well, like you just watched *The Texas Chain Saw Massacre.* Shake the jar really well, too
4. Pour over salad immediately before serving, and toss well
5. Decorate with flowers

Tongues of beef

Lange de beof.
Take þo ox tonge and schalle hit wele,
Sethe hit, broche hit in larde yche dele,
With cloves of gelofer hit broch þou shalle,
Þen do hit to fyre and rost hit alle;
With 3olkes of eyren enbene hit ay
Whille þat hit rostes, as I þe say.
Þen take blode, þat is so lefe,
Welle hit in fresshe brothe of þe befe,
Bray hit fulle wele in on mortere,
Do in fayre grece, þat is so clere;
Fors hit with spicys ry3t gode with alle,
And syrthun, serve hit in to þe halle;
To þe forsayde tonge þis sawce is dy3t,
Here endes oure potage fulle gode ry3t
~ Liber Cure Cocorum

Stewed Pigeons

Peions istued.
Take peions and hew hom in morselle smalle,
Put hom in a erþyn pot, þou shalle;
Take pilled garlek and herbys anon,
Hack hom smalle er þou more don;
Put hom in þo pot, and þer to take
Gode brothe with wyte grece, þou no3t forsake;
Do powdur þer to and gode verius,
Coloure hit with safron, and salt inow;
Þou put in pote þese þynges alle,
And stue þy peions þus þou schalle.
~ Liber Cure Cocorum

Turks Head Meat Pie

PREHEAT OVEN: 400 degrees F

Simple Short Crust Pasty

4-1/4 C. flour   2/3 C. melted butter
2 tsp salt   2/3 C. water

1. Mix salt and flour, melt butter over low heat, then stir in water
2. Make a well in the flour, pour in water and knead until stretchy
3. Let rest for thirty minutes, then roll out and shape into a pie pan

Meat:

2/3 lb minced pork or veal   1-1/4 C. dates
4 hindquarters rabbit   3/4 C. fresh crumbled cheese—
4 quails OR 2 partridges   sheep, goat, cow
    OR 2 pheasants   1-1/2 C. pistachios, no shells
2 tbsp sugar   2 tbsp honey
1/4 tsp ground cloves   lard, suet or butter
1 tsp ground cubeb or pepper   salt
1 egg (optional)

1. Season meat with salt and pepper, then brown in butter and cover
2. Simmer 40 minutes
3. Cool, remove bones, and cut into large chunks
4. Mix honey with two tbsp water, and warm
5. Steep dates five to ten minutes in honey
6. Drain dates, reserving honey, and cut dates in quarters
7. Combine meat, spices, cheese, dates, sugar, and in a bowl

The Pie

1. Grease a pie dish with butter, roll out dough, and shape into pie pan.
2. Fill pie with meat and cover with pistachio nuts.
3. Cover pie with dough, crimping edges to seal, and poke vent holes, which can become the eyes or the mouth in your 'Turk's Head.'
4. Use leftover dough to create a face—nose, eyebrows, mouth
5. Optional: baste the pie with egg white (light glaze) or egg yolk (dark glaze)
6. Bake pie in middle of oven, about 40 minutes
7. Let cool for five minutes before removing from pan
8. Decorate after baking: apply food color paste with a small brush, and gold leaf or silver foil

Cubeb pepper, often called for in medieval cooking, is also called Java pepper, or tailed pepper. It is peppery and a bit bitter. You can substitute black pepper with allspice.

Gold leaf and silver leaf, believe it or not, are edible! You might find 'booklets' of them at art supply stores.

Sauce for Swans

Sawce for swannus.
Take þo offal and þo lyver of þo swan,
In gode brothe þou sethe hom þan;
When hit is sothyne, take oute þe bonus,
Smalle hew þo flesshe, Syr, for þe nonus;
Make alyoure of crust of brede,
Of blode of swanne, þat soþun is lede,
Caste powdur of gynger and clawes þer to,
Of peper and wyn þou take also,
And salt hit þen and sethe hit wele;
Cast in þy flesshe, hewen yche a dele,
And messe hit forthe, as I þe kenne,
Set hit in sale before goode menne
~ Liber Cure Cocorum

Entrails for Wild Ducks, Swans, and Pigs

> Þandon for wylde digges, swannus, and piggus.
> Take, wasshe þo isues of swannes anon,
> And skoure þo guttus with salt ichon;
> Sethe alle to gedur and hew hit smalle,
> Þe flesshe and eke þo guttus with alle;
> Take galingale and gode gyngere
> And canel, and grynd hom al in fere;
> And myude bred þou take þerto,
> And temper hit up with brothe also;
> Coloure hit with brend bred or with blode,
> Seson hit with venegur, a lytelle for gode;
> Welle alle togedur in a posnet;
> In service forthe þou schalt hit sett.
> ~ Liber Cure Cocorum

Strawberry Pudding

Pudding made with wine! I'm thinking you can't go wrong serving pudding made with wine to a bunch of medieval warriors. And possibly Arundel's force had had their fill of alcoholic pudding and were therefore in no shape to meet the fierce James!

1 pt almond milk	2 tsp rice flour
large punnet of strawberries	1/3 C. sugar
1/2 C. red wine	1 tsp butter

1. Hull and quarter strawberries, leave in a bowl with wine for 15 minutes, and drain wine
2. Heat almond milk, butter, sugar, and rice flour together, stirring until thick
3. Add strawberries, pour into a large bowl and leave to cool
4. *Voila!* Warrior Pudding!

On Medieval Oranges

Here is the fun part of culinary research: words do not always mean what we think they mean. At first glance, it seems easy enough to recreate a recipe calling for oranges. On some digging, however, it turns out that the sweet orange we know, *citrus sinencis*, did not appear in Europe until the fifteenth century—about a hundred years too late for James Douglas's housewarming at Lintalee.

What his cooks would have used was *citrus aurantium*, an orange so bitter that it only tasted good if it was cooked or candied. If you can find bitter oranges, use them and eliminate the lemon juice/grapefruit juice. If not, use them to temper the sweetness of our modern oranges.

In the world of medieval thought on food, fruits that grew in the air —that is, on trees—were considered more proper for the upper classes.

Chicken with Rosewater

In summer the sauce for a roast chicken is half vinegar, half rose-water, and chilled. Orange juice is good with this.

PREHEAT OVEN: 350 degrees F

3 lbs boneless, skinless chicken 1/3 C. lemon juice
3 tbsp butter 2/3 C. juice squeezed from oranges
2/3 C. white wine vinegar salt to taste
2/3 C. rosewater

1. Melt butter in a skillet, brown chicken on both sides, and set aside
2. Add all other ingredients into same skillet, whisk together, and bring to a boil
3. Reduce heat, return chicken to pan, cover, and simmer for 35 to 45 minutes

ALTERNATE DIRECTIONS, since the original recipe doesn't say whether the chicken is boiled or baked:

1. Bake your chicken for 30 minutes at 400 degrees F
2. Lower heat to 350 F and bake for another 10 to 30 minutes, until the juices run clear when the chicken is pierced with a knife
3. Mix the sauce ingredients with juices from the roasting pan and pour over the chicken before serving.

Pigeon Breasts

Season your pigeons with peper / saffron / cloves and mace / with vergis and salt / then put them into your paest and so close them vp / and bake them / these will bake in halfe an houre / then take them forth / and if ye thynke them drye take a litle vergis and butter and put to them and so serue them.

1545, A Propre new booke of Cokery

PREHEAT OVEN: 350 degrees F

10 pigeon breasts	1/2 lb mushrooms
1 large onion	1 C. finely chopped shallots
1 stick celery	1 tbsp tomato paste
1 small leek	2-1/2 C. game or chicken stock
1 carrot	10 black peppercorns
olive oil	1 sprig of rosemary
1/2 chicken livers	10 sage leaves
1/2 lb pancetta lardons	a pinch of thyme
(or bacon)	16 oz. shortcrust pastry

1. Dice pigeon; slice onions, celery, leek, and carrot
2. Fry pigeon, chicken livers and pancetta in 1 tbsp olive oil until lightly browned, and put in a pie dish.
3. Fry onion, celery, leek and carrot in another tbsp of oil until golden, then add to pie dish
4. Fry mushrooms and shallots in (surprise!) *more* oil and (surprise again!) add to pie dish
5. Add tomato paste to pan; cook for 1 minute
6. Add stock and scrape up remnants of fried goods
7. Add peppercorns, rosemary, sage and thyme to stock
8. Bring to a boil
9. Pour stock over meat in the pie dish
10. Roll out pastry, cover pie, and bake 45 minutes

The Chicken that Comes to Life

Every dog must have its every day, and every feast must have its every subtlety. Let's give James Douglas the *Chicken that Comes to Life*. This will likely be far too distasteful for any modern reader—apart from the fact that many of my modern readers probably don't have live chickens around.

However, I can see James Douglas and his men, building his home practically in England's backyard, celebrating and laughing, and being delighted with the surprise of their dinner suddenly jumping up and running down the table. I can see those who have seen this before laughing heartily at some younger men who haven't, as the chicken runs over their trenchers, shocking and surprising them, flapping wings, and most likely sending a goblet or two of ale flying. The process was this:

1. Pluck a chicken (or any bird) alive, under hot water. (This is the part that would be distasteful to modern readers.)
2. Beat the yolks of two or three eggs with with powdered saffron and wheat flour
3. Distemper them with fat broth or the drippings from a roast
4. Paint the chicken so it is looks the color and texture of roasted meat.
5. Just before it is to be served, put the chicken's head under its wing, and rotate it until it falls asleep, then set this sleeping 'roast' chicken on a platter with the other meats.
6. Now—watch the fun when it suddenly wakes up and runs up and down the table!

Caledonia with Jimmy

Shawn's jaw tightened. He stared at the colorful bills lying wrinkled on the table. "There you go now," a voice said, and a plate with a hamburger slid into his view.

"Thanks," Shawn muttered. He heard the soft clink of Jimmy's plate touching down across the table. The man didn't move, didn't say a word.

Shawn looked up. "A job?" he suggested.

"Can I find you a job?" Jimmy snorted. "Daein whit? Playn yer horn wi ye?" He laughed scathingly, an eruption of sound that reddened his face and drew the startled attention of several diners. He waved his arm, and added, "Mibbe a could lead yer orchestra?" He looked around at the growing number of people looking his way. He laughed harshly, calling to his new-found audience,

Burger

2 lbs ground beef	1 dash celery salt
1 small onion, chopped very fine	1 dash pepper
2 tbsp horseradish	6 oz. butter
2 tbsp Worcestershire sauce	3 tsp Tabasco sauce
1 oz. garlic, finely diced	1 tsp crushed red pepper

1. Mix softened butter in bowl with 1 tsp tabasco sauce and 1 tsp crushed red pepper
2. Use plastic wrap to roll butter mixture into a log put in refrigerator to chill
3. Mix remaining ingredients together
4. Remove plastic wrap from butter log and cut butter into discs
5. Shape ground beef into 6 ounce balls; put a disc of butter into the middle of each
6. Flatten into patties, no more than an inch think
7. Grill and serve

Angus Discovers Simon's Origins

The aroma of baking chicken filled the room as he turned on the third. After the fourth, he took his dinner from the oven, leaving it out to cool. He glanced around his small kitchen. Irritation filled him, imagining Shawn's kitchen. It probably had acre-long slabs of shining granite counters, and gleaming, elegantly arched faucets, and slate floors, like he'd seen on movies of American homes. Of *course* she hadn't come back. Why should she? Grabbing a Guinness from the small refrigerator under the counter, Angus returned to the front room, and pulled up the final video. If he found nothing here, he had to think up another idea.

Something rustled outside the window. He looked up. Dark night stared in blankly above the lace. There was no more sound.

Chicken in Heather

PREHEAT OVEN: 375 degrees F

1 whole chicken, minus the giblets	3 oz. French mustard
3 oz. light cooking oil	1/2 tsp curry powder
4 oz. clear heather honey	1 clove chopped garlic
salt and pepper	

1. Mix cooking oil, honey, and spices together and pour over chicken in a pan
1. Cover and bake 1 hour
2. Baste chicken with juices and sauce; bake 30 minutes uncovered

Boar Fight

He had to keep the boar away from the baby. He barreled through the drooping branches. They scratched his face, tore his shirt, and grasped his cloak, but he burst out into the forest. "Here, I'm here!" he shouted, drawing the boar's attention. Blood flowed from the animal's left shoulder. It turned, sizing him up with beady eyes, and lowered its head. Niall crouched, knife and sword up. "Hugh!" he bellowed. "Owen!" It charged. Niall lunged aside, barely avoiding the jagged tusks, spun, and swung his sword down, slashing the animal's back. Blood trailed down its side. It gave a vicious snort, wheeled, and thrust its tusks up.

...

MacDonald's eyebrows beetled over his eyes. Without a word, he stalked past the man, and seated himself on his throne-like chair at the head of the hall. He lifted a hand, summoning his own steward, waiting by the door to the kitchens. The man rushed forward and dropped to one knee, head bowed. "My Lord?" "Bring me ale and meat. Is the boar being slaughtered?"

"They've begun, my Lord. 'Twill be ready for the evening meal." "Very good. The head on a platter, and tell my minstrel to compose a song. Sir Niall fought it single-handedly. Be quick with the ale."

Hunting Song, Sir Walter Scott

Waken, lords and ladies gay,
On the mountain dawns the day;
All the jolly chase is here
With hawk and horse and hunting-spear,
Hounds are in their couples yelling,
Hawks are whistling, horns are knelling,
Merrily, merrily mingle they
Waken, lords and ladies gay.

Waken, lords and ladies gay,
The mist has left the mountain gray;
Springlets in the dawn are steaming,
Diamonds on the brake are gleaming;
And foresters have busy been
To track the buck in thicket green;
Now we come to chant our lay,
Waken, lords and ladies gay.

Waken, lords and ladies gay,
To the greenwood haste away;
We can show you where he lies,
Fleet of foot and tall of size;
We can show the marks he made
When 'gainst the oak his antlers fray'd;
You shall see him brought to bay
Waken, lords and ladies gay.

Louder, louder chant the lay,
Waken, lords and ladies gay!
Tell them youth and mirth and glee
Run a course as well as we;
Time, stern huntsman! who can balk,
Staunch as hound and fleet as hawk:
Think of this, and rise with day,
Gentle lords and ladies gay!

Wild Boar

Wild boar, as a rule, should be cooked at lower temperatures than other meats: low and slow. When a boar dies after a chase or a prolonged, slow death, the meat is likely to be tougher. Marinades of pineapple juice, beer, and wine act as natural tenderizers. Glenmirril's cooks would have opted for wine, of course. They may have left the fat on the meat as it cooked, to help it 'baste' and become succulent.

Smoking, or slow cooking, is a common and preferred cooking method for wild pork even today. The basic idea is to wrap the meat, with your choice of seasonings, to hold in vapors and drippings, then slow smoke, (or bake at about 275 to 300 degrees F) rotating regularly. A whole boar will take all day, or overnight. Quarters generally take 5 to 6 hours, so the minstrel doesn't have much time to compose and learn a new song about Niall's deed!

Wild Boar Roast with Cranberry Sauce

1 wild boar roast	celery
1 bottle of red wine	salt, oil
1 C. water	1/2 C. cream
3 cloves	1/4 C. flour
4 juniper berries	2 C. of cranberries
1 bay leaf	clove powder
10 pepper corns	

1. Combine wine, water, cloves, juniper berries, bay leaf, pepper corns, and celery
2. Marinade roast overnight
3. Dry roast, salt lightly, then fry in oil in pot
4. Strain leftover marinade over roast
5. Cook well over medium heat, remove, and slice
6. Again, strain marinade from pot over roast
7. Mix cream and flour well and add to marinade in pot
8. Add cranberries and cook until thick, stirring constantly
9. Whisk in salt and clove powder and pour over roast

Ice Cream with Sophie, Emma, and Jon

Emma and Sophie were carrying banana splits to the table when Shawn and Aaron arrived with Jon. Emma dropped her bowl on the table and ran to Shawn, hugging his leg and chanting, "Mr. Finer! Mr. Finer!" Shawn laughed, though his heart did a funny flop at her innocent acceptance and love—healing balm after the snubs in the green room.

Cookie Ice Cream

Just for fun—one of the easiest ways to make ice cream at home. Be aware that there's a small risk of salmonella from raw eggs. Using clean, fresh, grade A or AA eggs reduces the risk.

3 egg yolks	1 C. crushed chocolate sandwich cookies
14 oz. condensed milk	2 C. heavy cream, whipped
4 tsp vanilla extract	

1. Beat egg yolks, then stir in condensed milk and vanilla
2. Stir in cookies and whipped cream
3. Pour it into a 9 by 5 loaf pan lined with foil
4. Cover and freeze for about 6 hours

Mrs. MacGonagle's Roast

"You're losing weight, Angus," she said sternly, when she had him cornered at her kitchen table. "Are you taking care of yourself?"

"I am, Mrs. MacGonagle," he reassured her with a smile. "Do you not see the groceries?"

She sniffed as she set a roast, rich vegetables swimming in a dark sauce, on the table. "It's that girl. The one who was...." She lowered her voice. "Pregnant. She took off with that American musician, did she not?"

"She's in America for Christmas." Angus sidestepped the issue of Shawn. The truth was, he realized, it had been since June he'd lost his taste for cooking, for eating, for much of anything, really.

"You're a far better man," Mrs. MacGonagle snipped, her nose in the air. "She's a fool, going with him."

"It smells grand, Mrs. MacGonagle," Angus said. "Shall we say grace?"

She removed her apron before settling herself, hands folded, and murmuring words of thanks. She looked up expectantly.

He rose, dipping the serving fork and knife in, and carving off a rich piece of meat for her. He spooned up a ladle full of carrots and potatoes onto her plate, and served himself.

Beef and Ale Pot Roast

PREHEAT OVEN: 325 degrees F

2 -/2 lb lean beef brisket	2 bay leaves
1 tbsp oil	pepper
2 red onions, quartered	3/4 pt beef stock
6 to 8 baby carrots, peeled	1/4 pt dark ale
4 sticks celery, sliced	1-1/2 tbsp gravy granules
6 potatoes	

1. Heat oil in a pot, add brisket, and brown all sides
2. Move to a deep ovenproof casserole dish; add onions, potatoes, carrots, celery, and bay leaves
3. Pour stock and brown ale over everything and cover with a tight fitting lid
4. Cook for 2 hours
5. Optionally, use gravy granules to thicken

Pot Roast in Red Wine

PREHEAT OVEN: 350 degrees F

1-1/2 lbs boneless beef chuck roast	1/2 C. pearl onions
1-1/2 lbs lamb	1/2 tsp dried marjoram
2 tbsp all-purpose flour	1/2 tsp dried thyme
2 tbsp canola oil	1 tsp salt
1/2 C. water	1/4 tsp pepper
1/2 C. red wine	1 onion, sliced
1 tsp dried basil	6 red potatoes
	6 carrots

1. Heat oil in an oven-proof pot with a lid over medium-high heat
2. Sprinkle beef and lamb with flour, then brown meat on all sides, about 10 minutes total
3. Remove from heat and add water, wine, seasonings, and onion slices
4. Replace cover and bake for 3 hours
5. Clean potatoes and slice in half; peel carrots and cut into 2 inch lengths
6. Add potatoes, carrots, and pearl onions to roast
7. Add water if roast looks dry
8. Bake, covered, until roast pulls apart easily with a fork, about another hour.

What Happened with Angus?

"It's been over a week." Amy laid down her fork as she finished Shawn's meatloaf. He'd added haggis, and she would gladly have eaten the whole pan, it tasted so good. "What happened with Angus?"

"You like the meatloaf?" he asked.

"Leave it to you to outdo the Scots on their own specialty. What did Angus say?"

Shawn rose from the table, clearing his plate and hers. "Is James asleep?"

"I heard him playing in there. What happened with Angus?"

"Ben's got eight concerts lined...."

Amy raised her eyebrows.

Shawn's Meatloaf

PREHEAT OVEN: 350 degrees F

1 tbsp butter	7 butter crackers, crushed
1/4 C. minced onion	1 egg, lightly beaten
2 cloves garlic, minced	3-1/2 tbsp sour cream
1-1/2 tsp salt	1-1/2 tbs Worcestershire sauce
1-1/2 tsp pepper	15 oz. tomato sauce, divided
2 lbs extra-lean ground beef	1/4 C. milk (optional)
3 slices toast, crumbled	3 tbsp ketchup

1. Saute onion in butter and garlic over medium heat until tender
2. Remove from heat, and season with salt and pepper.
3. Mix onion and garlic, beef, crumbled bread, crushed crackers, egg, sour cream, Worcestershire sauce, and 1/2 of the tomato sauce
4. Stir in milk 1 tsp at a time—mixture should be moist, but not soggy
5. Pat into a 5x9 inch loaf pan
6. Bake uncovered for 40 minutes
7. Increase temperature to 400 degrees F and bake another 15 minutes
8. Mix remaining tomato sauce and ketchup. Pour over the top of the meatloaf, and continue baking 10 minutes.

Monadhliath's Orchards

As dawn broke, Simon stopped on a barren crest, peering with raised hand into the rising sun, where it laced the undersides of clouds, gold and pink. He gazed down in satisfaction over the orchards spreading around the ancient monastery. The rising sun lit the church tower and the great stone walls that had stood for eons. Their bell tolled, low and mournful, great slow swings of the huge beast, its voice sounding a deep cry of anguish on every fourth beat.

Compote of Apples and Almonds

Because this is a recipe for curing illness, it specifies exact amounts. In medieval times, sugar was regarded as a form of medicine. It seems Mary Poppins carried on the tradition in her own way. Tart apples are preferred.

2-1/2 lbs of whole apples	1/2 pt water
2 C. powdered almonds	salt
1/2 C. sugar	

1. Peel and dice apples
2. Boil water, add apple, and cook covered 10 to 15 minutes
3. Drain apple, saving the water.
4. Add powdered almonds to cooking water; set aside for 1hr
5. Drain almond milk through cheesecloth, pressing pulp firmly
6. Boil almond milk with a pinch of salt, add minced apples and sugar
7. Serve cold

Simon Demands Entry to Monadhliath

Simon yanked the cord again, and again, and again. The bell cried out. Simon leaned into the iron bars, searching the grounds. They couldn't all have left. He gave it one last, angry yank.

From around the church, tottered a bent old monk, carrying a basket against his brown robe.

"You!" Simon called. The monk continued to the garden, dropping to his knees and pulling a spade from the basket.

"You!" Simon shouted. "The Lord of Claverock summons you!"

On hands and knees, the old man dug in rich loam.

The Monks' Garden Orchard Soup

While this is not an authentic medieval recipe, it uses food from the monks' vegetable garden and orchard both. I think they would have freely experimented with everything they had and easily come up with this.

3 apples	1/2 C. single cream
2 C. parsnip	salt
1 onion	white pepper
2 oz. butter	Parmesan cheese
4 C. milk	parsley

1. Peel parsnips and apples and quarter
2. Dice onion very finely
3. Saute onions in butter, stirring occasionally
4. Add parsnips and apples and cook for five minutes
5. Pour in just enough milk to cover all, and bring to a boil
6. Reduce heat and simmer 15 to 20 minutes, until parsnips are tender
7. Remove from heat; add cream.
8. Return to low heat, stirring continuously. Do not boil.
9. Mix soup vigorously, and then even more vigorously
10. Add salt and pepper.
11. Garnish with Parmesan cheese and parsley

Medieval Salad

4 C. cabbage, sliced thin
2 C. radicchio, sliced thin
6 apples, peeled, sliced very thin
3 bunches parsley
5 C. beets
2 C. almonds
2 C. prunes
2 C. dried or fresh figs
2 C. dates

Vinaigrette:
3 tbsp lemon juice
2/3 C. olive oil
2 tsp grated lemon zest
1/2 tsp sugar
salt and pepper

1. Whisk together lemon juice, zest, sugar, salt, and pepper until sugar is dissolved
2. Pour in oil in a slow, steady stream, whisking steadily
3. Toss cabbage, radicchio, beets, and apples with vinaigrette
4. Arrange artistically with dried fruit and nuts—yes, this is a 'recipe' that tells you to play with your food! Have fun! Make patterns, pictures, designs! If you are a medieval knight, you might like to make your coat of arms—or, rather, tell your cook to make your coat of arms on each salad!

Bonus Section: Cooking with Shawn

Shrimp and Crab Ravioli

Check what's in the fridge.

Grab leftover shrimp and crab ravioli, previously made from a bag meal, with Italian seasoning and cream of broccoli soup added

Put pot on stove on low, add water to make sure cream of broccoli sauce doesn't burn while practicing trombone

Glance at pot—looks kind of boring

Check fridge—grab left over pre-cooked ham; dice and add

Onions on counter—better use them while they're still good! Dice half an onion and add

Notice walnuts in bag on counter, meant for cookies— walnuts are good! Thrown in a handful—not chopped because trombone is calling

Looks like it might take awhile at 1—turn heat up to 3

Play D minor harmonic scale, 2 octaves, do a little improv, jot down cool solo on manuscript paper

Check ravioli—not burned yet, not bubbling, either. Turn heat to 5

Run through *Vox Gabrieli*

Hear bubbling—check ravioli—looking good!

Stew in Red Wine

Grill stew meat—however much you have or want

Chop and saute two onions with the meat as it cooks. Add more if you like. Probably not less. If Amy's nephews are around, distract them from the onions with a long and funny story, and hope they don't notice

Add red wine. Add a little more. If Amy's nephews are around, don't do it in front of them.

Add basil and Italian seasoning, because there's no thyme....that was a little musician humor. Laugh till your stomach hurts at your musician humor.

Add garlic because everything should have garlic

Add paprika—just a dash, though—because red is a good color

Add a bag of frozen roasted potatoes and green beans

Needs something—liquid looks low. Add water.

Add a spoonful of cornstarch as a thickening agent (yeah, I know what a thickening agent is)

Dump in a bag of frozen peas and carrots and add more water

What the heck—add more red wine. Just crank the nozzle and let it flow Red wine is good for the heart

Add salt and pepper. Taste.

Add more salt and pepper, more Italian seasoning

Medieval Almond Chicken in White Sauce

Start with a medieval-inspired almond chicken recipe on the internet.

Boil white rice.

Sliver almonds.

Substitute whatever cream of chicken soup you have for whatever the recipe called for. Or use the cream of celery soup. I used cream of mushroom and cream of broccoli.

When the boneless, skinless chicken is thawed, roll it and coat it in finely ground up bread crumbs. Amy's nephews should do a pretty good job at mashing bread as fine as sand.

Discover the 14 year old nephew didn't buy the bread you told him to and there's only one heel left. Substitute crumbled ginger cookies and crumbled Cookies of Joy freshly made today from Hildegard of Bingen's books. Or substitute chips or ground up breakfast cereal of some sort. Anything that can be ground down to powder and used to coat the chicken.

Coat the chicken. Pan broil it until brown. That should be 3 to 5 minutes per side. If Amy's nephew put the wrong chicken, legs full of bones, in to defrost, it's going to be a lot longer. Probably you should fry up some onions with the chicken and mix them into the rice when they're sauteed.

Put the cooked rice on the bottom of a 9x13 pan.

Mix together soup, ranch dressing, grated cheese and almonds. Recipe called for cheddar. I didn't have any. I'm sure mozzarella will work just fine. Keep pouring in ranch dressing until it looks good. Good is subjective. Is it smooth and remotely liquidy? I guess that's good.

Put the coated, pan-fried chicken on top of the rice and cover it thoroughly with the cheese and almond white sauce.

Cook at 400 degrees Fahrenheit for 40 minutes.

Dessert/ Afterword

Every tasty smorgasboard must have a fine ending!
I'm not sure I have a *fine* ending, but at least it can be light—as the medievals recommended finishing a meal, and as we ourselves do. (By the way, did you catch that musical pun...*fine!* Yes, this is the *fine,* the *ending,* even if it's not a *fine* ending.)

I hope you've enjoyed this romp in thyme...and cinnamon, nutmeg, and cloves, in engastration and flying pies and singing and fire-breathing roasts!

I hope you've enjoyed the whimsical and creative mind of medieval cooks and are inspired in your own cooking. I thought it was appropriate to end it with a short selection of *Cooking with Shawn,* because this is something that was really brought home to me, the more I researched recipes: in our modern day, we often think of cooking as a set of directions, a skill, a science with precise measurements and times. In truth, I think it is more like music or art: some basic general knowledge about the materials, mixed with creativity and fun..

In our modern age, food has become too often utilitarian—a harried trip through the fast food drive-through to stuff in some calories and hopefully a few nutrients. In contrast, a medieval meal was often a leisurely social event, a time to relax and, at least in the castles, enjoy song and jugglers and the company of many others, along with the wonderful variety of dishes. I believe these things are nourishing not merely to the body, but to the emotions, the psyche, the soul.

Another Sidebar Story

Regarding nourishment of the soul, I started with a couple of sidebar stories, and I'll finish with a couple. When I was 18, I had a very bad year. I left home, returned to my college dorm, paid everything I had to ensure at least one more semester of college, and began working two jobs—16 hours a day, sleeping two or three hours between each shift. It was a terrible summer.

What I have always remembered of that time, however, is a friend who lived just down the hall, also self-sufficient at 18. The day I arrived, she appeared at my door. I'm not sure she said a thing; just smiled and handed me a box full of food. Bread. Ramen noodles. Peanut butter maybe.

Simple food and a simple gesture, but powerful. Why? Because food nourishes not merely our bodies, but our souls.

In a sidebar to that sidebar (I have to keep the book symmetrical!), I thought of this incident when, shortly before publication, I joined Karen Olson Johnson and Laura Hedlund on their Food Freedom radio program early one Saturday morning. We had a great talk afterward, but I had to cut it short to get to work. I mentioned I'd be teaching for 8 hours straight and had to get food on the way, to eat during the day. Karen immediately opened her bag and offered me granola bars to take along.

Once again, a simple gesture, but profound. As quoted earlier:

The nourishment of body is food, while the nourishment of the soul is feeding others.

~ Alī ibn Abī Ṭālib, Caliph

Have I wandered from the main point of the book? Or started a new book? I think, in fact, this was common knowledge to the medievals and affected their feasts and food.

In conclusion, I hope you will see this book as just a start, and be inspired to look further into the things presented here, the history, the food, the old wisdom about what various herbs, spices, and foods did for our spiritual and emotional well-being, and more.

I hope you will try some of these recipes for fun and nourishment, to feed others, to nourish your soul and theirs—not the porpoise frumenty, though—and let me know on my facebook page or blog how it turned out.

BIBLIOGRAPHY: Books

A Citizen of Paris. *Le ménagier de Paris: traité de morale et d'économie domestique composé vers 1393.* Paris. De L'Imprimerie de Crapelet. 1846

Aresty, Esther B. *The Delectable Past.* New York, NY. Simon and Schuster. 1964

Coulton, G.G., editor, and Power, Eileen, translator. "Citizen of Paris," author, c. 1393. reprinted as *The Goodman of Paris.* London. George Rutledge and Sons. 1928

de Mauduit, Vicomte. Introductions by Francis, Countess of Warwick and Elizabeth Craig, MCA, MIH. *The Viscomte in the Kitchen.* New York. Covici-Friede Publishers. 1934

Diehl, Daniel and Donnely, Mark P. *Medieval Celebrations: Your Guide to Planning and Hosting Spectacular Feasts, Parties, Weddings, and Renaissance Fairs.* Mechanicsburg, PA. Stackpole Books. 2011

Fournier-Rosset, Jany. *From Saint Hildegard's Kitchen: Foods of Health, Foods of Joy.* Ligouri, Missouri. Ligouri Publications. 2010

Mortimer, Ian. *The Time Traveler's Guide to Medieval England: A Handbook for Visitors to the 14th Century.* New York, New York. Simon and Schuster, Inc. 2008

Murray, Janet. *Traditional Scots Recipes.* New York, NY. Bramhall House. 1972

Strehlow, Dr. Wighard. *Hildegard of Bingen's Spiritual Remedies.* Rochester, VT. Healing Arts Press. 2002

von Bingen, Hildegard. *Physica: The Complete English Translation of her Classic Work on Health and Healing.* Rochester, VT. Healing Arts Press. 1998, Translator: Thorpe, Priscilla

Wickham, Dynthia. *Herbs: Growing, drying and using herbs—from cooking to cosmetics.* Secaucus, NJ. Castle Books. 1973

Widcome, Richard. *The Cheese Book.* Seacaucus: Chartwell Books, 1978. via http://www.godecookery.com/how2cook/cheesnet.htm

Internet

Food.com
recipes.com
germanfood.about.com
anniesremedy.com
medievalplus.com
britishfood.about.com
familyoven.com
historylearningsite.co.uk
whiskyfacts.com
homecooking.about.com
bbc.co.uk
foodandwine.com
foodnetwork.com
YouTube's Hackaweek TV
cheesemaking.com
leaf.tv
iledefrancecheese.com
interestingandweird.com
medievalcookery.blogspot
karenmaitland.com
telusplanet.net on Viandier
godecooker.com
indefinitelywild.gizmodo.com

medievalhistories.com
bellavistaranch.com
medievalists.net
byo.com on medieval ale
coquinaria.nl
oraclaireland.com
timhodkinson.blogspot.com
oldcook.com
old.post-gazette.com
edwardthesecond.blogspot.com
medieval-spell.com
igourmet.com
ohnuts.com
nvg.org.au
medieval-recipes.com
thefinertimes.com
davidfriedman.com
culturesforhealth.com
eatingrules.com
brewery.org
herbology-101.blogspot.com
thefalconersdaughter.blogspot.com

Made in the USA
Lexington, KY
15 June 2017